INTRODUCING
·DESIGN·AND·
·COMMUNICATION·

RICHARD TUFNELL

Hutchinson

London Melbourne Sydney Auckland Johannesburg

Hutchinson and Co. (Publishers) Ltd
An imprint of the Hutchinson Publishing Group
Brookmount House, 62-65 Chandos Place, Covent Garden, London
WC2N 4NW

Hutchinson Publishing Group (Australia) Pty Ltd
16-22 Church Street, Hawthorn, Melbourne, Victoria 3122

Hutchinson Group (NZ) Ltd
32-34 View Road, PO Box 40-086, Glenfield, Aukland 10

Hutchinson Group (SA) (Pty) Ltd
PO Box 337, Bergvlei 2012, South Africa

First published 1986
© Richard Tufnell 1986

Designed and typeset in 11 on 13 pt Linotron Zapf Book Light
by The Pen and Ink Book Company Limited
Illustrated by the author and The Pen and Ink Book Company
Limited
Printed and bound in Great Britain by Scotprint Ltd., Musselburgh,
Scotland

British Library Cataloguing in Publication Data
Tufnell, Richard
    Introducing design and communication.
    1. Engineering drawings   2. Mechanical drawing
    I. Title
    604.2'4   T353

ISBN 0-09-160701-9

Acknowledgements

The author would like to thank the following for their help
in the preparation of this book: students from Middlesex
Polytechnic especially Graham Burt, Gary Calvert, Gill
Coxall, Bill Dexter, Barry Gillespie, Henry Hawes, Michael
Martin, Brian Porter, Terry Quirk, Geoff Pragnell and Gillian
Rogers; Valerie Tufnell for typing the manuscript and her
support and encouragement throughout the preparation
of the book.

The author is grateful to the following designers for their
assistance in the preparation of the final section, Designers
at Work: Nick Butler, BIB; Trevor Crocker, The Pack Design
Company; Roderick Ham, Roderick Ham and Partners; Jilly
Knight, Electronic Arts; Ron Saunders, Ogle Design; Angela
Simpson, Fitch and Company.

Acknowledgement is also due to the following for
permission to reproduce artwork: Esso UK Ltd. p.35;
Concept and design courtesy of General Electric Plastics
Europe p.35; The Consumers' Association p.59.

CONTENTS

Introduction

DESIGN AND COMMUNICATION

What is design?

Designing is an everyday activity. It is something we all do – often without even realizing it! Design is the way we solve problems and find the best solutions. The more thought and care that we take over finding a solution, the better it is likely to be. Every object in the man-made world has been designed. Most objects have been well designed. They are good to look at and they work efficiently. These two things about an object are called **form** (appearance) and **function**. Badly designed things often do not work properly, they may even break down. Also, they often do not look 'quite right'.

Communication

Every part of a design is important. To make a successful design, nothing can be left to chance. Ideas must be checked, tested and modified (altered), before the right solution is found. We cannot design things in our minds, because we would probably make mistakes. Instead, we have to explore our ideas using drawings and models. These give us a record of our thoughts, which we can use to work out solutions. As well as helping us 'talk to ourselves', drawings and models also let us talk to other people, so that we can get their advice. This is called **communication**. Communication is a vital part of designing. This book will help you communicate your ideas to other people. It will also help you understand design drawings made by someone else.

Starting design

Design is something you will do at school *and* at home. This is how you will look for the answer to a design problem. It is also a good way to go about solving most other problems.

A design problem starts with a **brief**. A design brief is a short statement which poses a problem.

Before you look for possible solutions to the problem, look carefully at the brief. Write down a list of the features which your design must take into account. This list of features is called a **specification**.

You may now need to do some **research** to find out more about the problem. To do this you may have to use books, magazines or video recordings. Or you may have to visit museums or get advice from an expert who knows more about the problem.

When you've finished your research you can start to **think up ideas**. You will have to check possible solutions with the specification. Eventually you will arrive at the right solution. This is the one which you think best meets the brief. Now you can complete the brief with the materials and resources you have been given in the time available.

You need to **develop** your chosen solution very carefully. You need to prepare drawings which you can use to make the final solution. You also have to plan how you are going to make your solution. Now you can make or **realize** your solution.

Finally, you must **test** your solution. You have to see how well your solution meets the brief. You have to see if any changes could improve the solution. You will not often make a perfect design, but you will learn a great deal from your mistakes!

WHAT SKILLS ARE INVOLVED?

This book will help you learn the skills and knowledge you need to do these things:

- Make simple sketches which you can use to explore solutions to design problems.
- Prepare working drawings in first and third angle orthographic projection.
- Produce presentation drawings using different drawing systems.
- Apply shade, shadow and colour to improve the visual quality (appearance) of your drawings.
- Make simple two-dimensional and three-dimensional models.
- Use correctly the common conventions and symbols used by designers.
- Choose the best type of drawing for a particlar task.
- Understand enough geometry to solve simple problems.

This book will help you to understand the following:

- The types of drawings and models designers use to help them find, develop and communicate ideas.
- The importance of graphics in everyday life.
- How computers are used in design and communication.

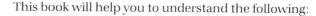

HOW TO USE THIS BOOK

She's looking at this page!!!

This book is divided into a number of sections. Each section deals with a particular topic. However, you may need information from one section of the book when you are working on another section. For example, the section on making models is towards the end of the book, but you may want to refer to it much sooner.

This is what you will find in each section:

- Details of the range of media (materials) which you may need for that section.
- Information about the constructions, techniques and procedures you will need to acquire the skills in that section. These are often listed as key points – a check list or a series of guidelines.
- A range of activities which will give you practice in the skills of design and communication.
- Every so often you will find the title 'Did you know'. These sections give interesting information about the instruments and media you will be using, or the things you will be drawing.

The last section of the book describes the work of some active designers. The types of drawings they use to communicate their ideas are similar to those you will learn about in the book.

Finally, there are some design projects. To tackle these successfully you will need to use the range of skills and techniques shown in the book.

This book will help you solve problems more efficiently. The skills which you will learn are ones which you will find useful, not just at school, but also at home, and later on at work. Once you master the basic skills, drawing is fun. Just like playing an instrument, or a game, the more you practise, the better your drawings will become!

COMMUNICATING IDEAS

Words

Words are important in design. A design brief is usually a written statement. Precise details are often described using words. Drawings often need explaining and notes can be added to make them clear. This is called **annotating** the drawing. It is important to be able to translate a written description of an object into a drawing.

Sketches

A **sketch** is the first time you will give an idea in your head real substance. Once on paper an idea can be changed, drawn from another view and generally explored. A sketch also gives you a record of each of your ideas. Sketching soon pinpoints the advantages and disadvantages of a possible solution.

Diagrams

A **diagram** is a drawing which helps to simplify a complicated system. Look at the illustration of the electronic circuit. It is very complicated and difficult to understand. The circuit diagram is more straightforward. As with most diagrams, symbols have been used to keep it simple. To understand the diagram you need to know what the symbols stand for. Other diagrams show how an operation is carried out. These are called **flow diagrams**.

Working drawings

When you have solved all the problems of the design brief, you must make a **working drawing**. This gives the precise details of every component. The number of drawings you need to describe accurately every component of a car or an aeroplane is vast! The working drawing is vital to make the final product meet the specification. These drawings are drawn in a special way. This means everyone can read them. This type of drawing is called an **orthographic projection**.

Pictorial drawings

Working drawings do not give a very good idea of how an object will finally appear. A **pictorial** or **presentation drawing** is needed as well. You can draw these in different ways. You might add colour to make the drawing more realistic. This is known as **rendering** the drawing.

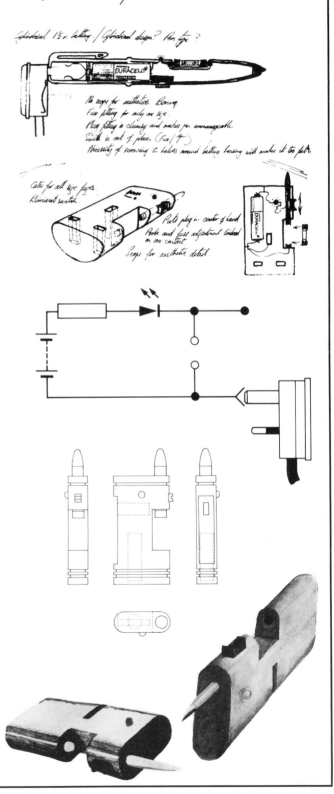

Exploded drawings

This type of drawing shows how an object fits together. From it you can see easily how one part relates to another.

Computer graphics

The computer is an invaluable aid to the designer. Complex drawings can be changed quickly if a fault is found. All the drawings for a complicated object can be stored in a very small space. It is easy and quick to recall them. You can store objects which you draw frequently in a library. Computers are also far more accurate than humans. Drawings produced on a computer are more precise than those made at a conventional drawing board.

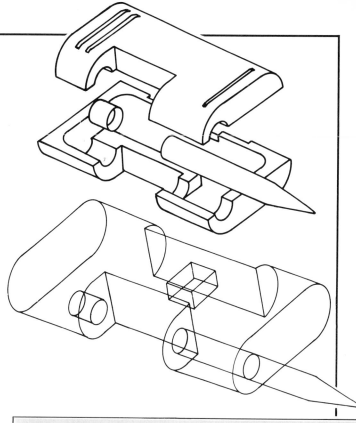

Models

Models can be used in many ways. They may be two-dimensional and used to test if a mechanism will work. Three-dimensional models will help you check out the appearance of an object. Models can be used at any stage in the design process. They can be 'rough and ready', made of scrap materials, just to check your first ideas. They can be extremely precise and accurate, the final test of your design. This type of model might be called a **prototype**. Models allow you to see all around an object. Computer programs also allow you to do this. For this reason, computer drawings are often described as models.

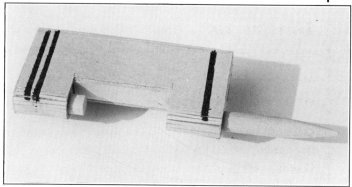

Photographs

The camera is very useful for recording information. You might use it to help your research or to photograph an idea. You can even make a photograph of your model more realistic than the model!

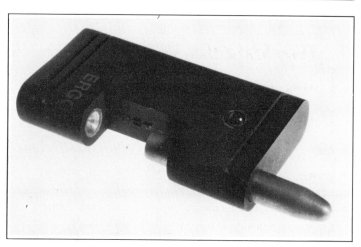

Activity 1   Make a folder in which you can keep your drawings. Drawings take a long time to produce, so you will want to look after them. Use stiff card, corrugated cardboard or plastic. First of all make a list of the important features of the folder. This is your specification. These questions may help you.

- *What size should it be?*
- *What will be the most useful shape?*
- *What material will be used?*
- *How strong must it be?*
- *How is it going to be made?*
- *Will it need to be carried around?*
- *How can the drawings be kept safe inside the folder?*

- *Is there any choice of colour of the material?*
- *How will you know that the folder is yours?*

You can see that designing is not straightforward. Once you start thinking about a problem, you must make many decisions. You will need advice and help from your teacher to find the best solution to this brief.

Getting started

BASIC MEDIA

Pencils

Ordinary lead pencils are probably the most versatile drawing tools there are. There are nineteen different types or **grades**. The hardest is a 9H pencil and the softest is an EE pencil. You will not need to use the whole range. For technical drawing a 2H or 4H is best. For freehand drawing an HB or 2B gives better results. When you shade a drawing you may find an even softer pencil such as a 4B useful.

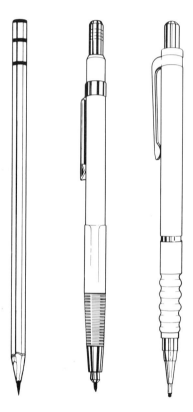

As well as ordinary wood pencils there is also a wide range of technical pencils. These are like propelling pencils. They are called **clutch pencils**. You get more lead out of the pencil by pushing a button on the opposite end to the lead. Leads are available in the full range of hardness and also in a range of colours. The leads are also made in a range of thicknesses. This makes it easy to get an even line width.

You need a good pencil sharpener to keep the point on your pencils. A small piece of abrasive paper will help you keep the point between sharpenings. If you use a knife to sharpen your pencils, make sure that the blade is sharp and *always* cut away from your body. With a knife you can produce either a drafting or needle point or a wedge end to your pencil. Different points are useful for different types of drawings.

Remember to take care of your pencils. The lead in a pencil will break if you drop it or use it for anything other than drawing, such as a drumstick or a dummy! Take care not to sharpen your pencil close to your drawing because the lead dust may cause dirty smudges.

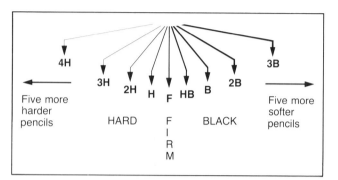

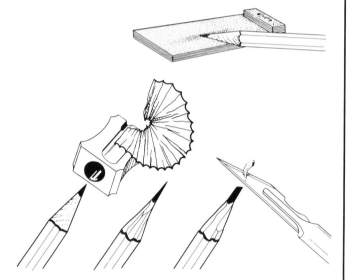

Did you know... *The name for a pencil comes from a Latin word which means a little tail. Lead pencils were unknown before the seventeenth century. In 1683, Sir Robert Pettus was the first person to glue graphite into a case of cedar wood and produce a pencil similar to those we use today. The hardness of a pencil depends on the grade of graphite used and the amount of clay which is mixed with it. The less clay, the softer the lead. Just in case you had not realized, a pencil is made from two pieces of wood with a groove down the centre. The two halves are glued together with the lead in place and then the outside of the pencil is shaped. If you look carefully you will notice that the lead in softer pencils is slightly larger in diameter than that in harder pencils. This is to give it the necessary strength.*

Activity 2 *Pencils can get difficult to hold when they become too short, but do not throw these stubs away. Instead, design and make a simple holder which will allow you to use these short ends. Take particular care that the holder weighs about the same as an ordinary pencil and has the same dimensions — any ideas?*

Pens and markers for drawing

The **ink pens** used by designers are known as **technical pens**. The nib of the pen is a tube. Ink is fed down this. The size of the tube determines the width of the line. There are nine standard sizes from 0.13 to 2.0 mm. Technical pens are very accurate. The most useful sizes are 0.35 to 0.5 mm.

You are probably familiar with **ball point pens** or **biros**. They can also be used for drawing, but take care because cheap ones smudge easily. Ballpoints give out ink via a steel or tungsten carbide ball that rolls. These pens come in a range of line widths and colours.

Roller pens look like ballpoints, but they have a smoother action and are cleaner to use. The ink is fed to the tungsten carbide ball via hundreds of microscopic glass beads. This guarantees an even flow of ink. A range of widths and colours is available.

Plastic tip pens are very good for writing. They produce accurate line widths, including very fine lines. A network of fine channels in the plastic nib allows the ink to be drawn to the tip by capillary action.

Fibre tip pens generally have a nylon or vinyl tip. The nibs of these pens vary from firm to supple. The nibs are often made of synthetic fibres bonded in resin. This gives them a long life. Fibre tips are also available that are similar to technical pens. They have tubular nibs and are available in the same size range.

Did you know... *A biro is called a biro because it was invented by a Hungarian called Lazlo Biro. He invented it in 1945, but his design was an expensive*

There is a very wide range of pens and markers which can be used for drawing. They can be divided into five groups: ink pens, ball points, roller pens, plastic tips and fibre tips.

When you choose a pen, try it out first and see if it produces the type of line you want. The wide range of pens available can be confusing and new types are constantly being introduced.

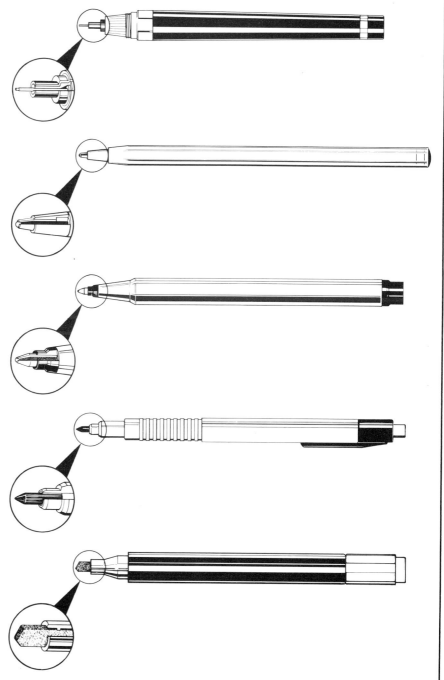

novelty. In 1956, a Frenchman, Baron Marcel Bich, designed the Bic crystal. It was cheap and dependable and an instant success. A new Bic ballpoint has a 'write out' length of over 2000 metres — not bad for the few pence it costs! About half a million biros are sold daily in Britain.
The fibre tip was a Japanese

invention. The original pen, produced in 1963, had a bamboo inner barrel which fed ink to the tip. In 1966 the bamboo was replaced with acrylic fibres. These prevented blotting. The 'write out' distance will depend on the width of the nib. A fine line roller pen will have a writing distance of around 3500 metres.

Erasing mistakes

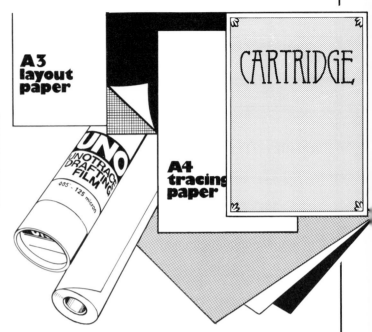

We all make mistakes and we sometimes need to remove marks we have made. There are different types of **erasers**, so make sure that you use the right one for the job. For pencil lines use a non-abrasive vinyl rubber or a soft 'putty' eraser. Ink is more difficult to remove. If you are drawing on tracing paper, there are special erasers which will remove the ink chemically. If you are working on paper, you can correct mistakes with the white correcting fluids typists use.

Key points

- Make sure that the eraser is clean by rubbing it on a clean piece of paper.
- Work in one direction, for example top to bottom.
- Blow or shake off the rubbings. This prevents you from smudging the drawing with your hand.
- Use the eraser in one direction. A 'scrubbing' action might crinkle the paper.
- Use a shield or mask to protect the rest of your drawing. You can buy thin stainless steel shields or make your own using thin styrene sheet.

Paper

What should you draw on? Look inside a graphics shop and you will see a bewildering range of papers. You need to know about a few of them. The most useful paper for design work is **layout paper**. It is sold in pads. A3 size is the most useful. You can see through layout paper so you can copy drawings, which is very helpful. **Cartridge paper** is a good quality all-purpose drawing paper. Use this for presentation drawings and for detailed working drawings. **Squared paper** is good for sketching. The squares give you guidelines for your drawings. **Tracing paper** or **plastic drafting film** is also useful, especially if you are doing ink drawings. Different coloured papers have many uses. Try to keep a range of papers and never throw any scraps away.

Did you know... *Paper is graded according to its size, weight and tooth.*

Size *You can get paper in a range of sizes known as the 'A' series. A0 is the largest size. It has an area of 1 square metre and measures 841 mm × 1189 mm. Fold it in half and you have A1, in half again for A2, and so on. This book is A4 size, 210 mm × 297 mm. The sides of each rectangle are in the ratio 1:2.*

Weight *The weight of paper is measured in grams per square metre – gsm. Layout paper is about 60 gsm and cartridge paper is between 100 and 120 gsm. The weight is a guide to the paper's thickness. The more it weighs, the thicker it is.*

Tooth *Tooth is a description of the surface texture of the paper (its roughness or smoothness). Smooth papers are good for fine line work. A paper with more tooth is good for pencil work. It can give a drawing more character.*

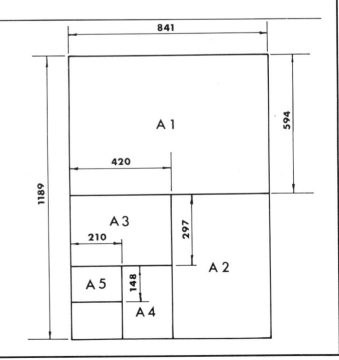

SCALE

When something is too large to fit on a piece of paper, it must be **drawn to scale**. When an architect designs a building or a cartographer draws a map they draw to scale. They must make things smaller to fit them on a piece of paper. This is called **scaling down**. Electronic engineers designing printed circuits have to **scale up** their drawings, making them larger. This helps them see what they are doing. The drawing of the car is scaled down. The drawing of it is 60 mm, but the car is really 3.6 m long. The car is drawn to a scale of 1:60. The drawing of the paperclip is 60 mm, but it is actually 30 mm long. The paperclip is drawn to a scale of 2:1.

Activity 3   *Measure a plug and the bung from a biro. Now measure the drawings below. Work out the scale of the drawings.*

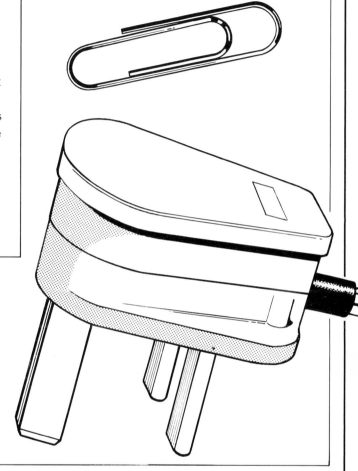

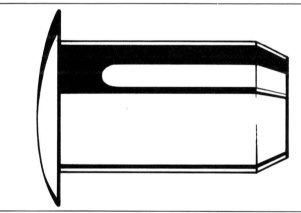

COPYING DRAWINGS

We often need to reproduce drawings. You may be copying a drawing from a book, or making a final drawing from a rough, or making a copy to use in the workshop. If you are using layout paper, you can see through it, so it is easy to copy the drawing. If you are using thicker paper, a **light box** might help you. A bright light in a box shines through an opaque surface. Your drawing is illuminated from below. You can now see it through the paper on which you are drawing. You may find a light box in the geography room. (It might be called a tracing table there.) You can use the sun and a window in the same way. Make sure the window is firmly shut, or only use a window which does not open.

Tracing is another method. Using tracing paper and a lead pencil can, however, be messy. You can buy clean tracing paper similar to carbon paper, or dressmaker's tracing paper.

DRAWING WITH A PENCIL

Key points

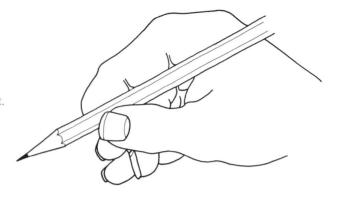

- Hold the pencil in the most comfortable way. If you are not sure, look at the picture opposite. It shows the most common way. The lower picture shows you how to hold the pencil when shading.
- Hold the pencil about 20 to 30 mm from the point.
- Do not rest your hand on the paper. Hold it just above and use your little finger as a guide.
- Do not grip the pencil tightly.
- Keep your wrist firm and draw with your whole arm.
- Do not fix your paper down if you are sketching. Have it free to move around, holding it steady with your free hand.
- Do not sketch on a hard surface such as formica. A piece of card provides a good surface. If you use a drawing pad, slip the card under the sheet on which you wish to draw. Alternatively, turn the paper over so that it rests on the card at the back of the pad.
- Use a soft pencil for sketching, HB or softer.

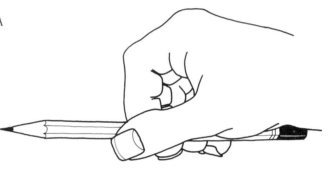

Loosening up

When you play a game, you loosen up or have a 'kick around' before you start seriously. Try doing the same when drawing. Do these exercises using a soft pencil and freehand – no cheating!

Make a series of straight lines. Do it quickly and do not let the pencil leave the paper. Try to make the lines parallel. Make the lines look as if they lie between parallel lines. Vary the direction of the lines and the pressure you apply.

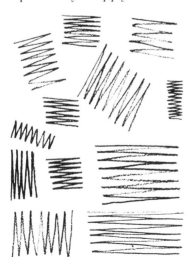

Now practise circular shapes. Hold the pencil above the paper and make circular movements on the paper with your little finger. Gradually lower the pencil to the paper and start drawing circles. Relax the pressure on the pencil as you draw the circles. Do it over and over again, until you get the feel of drawing circles.

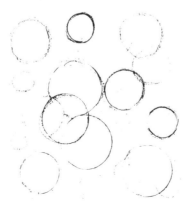

Next try some straight lines. Start with a series of parallel lines, horizontally across the page. Do not worry about the length. Concentrate on the direction. Then try some vertical lines and some diagonal lines. As you improve, draw longer lines. You will find it gets more difficult.

Drawing shapes

Freehand lines present no problem. Now you can begin to use them. Start with squares and rectangles. When you draw a line, think about its direction only. Another line will fix its length. If your line is not quite right, do not worry – try again. Draw as many rectangles and squares as you need to get the right feel. Now try some triangles.

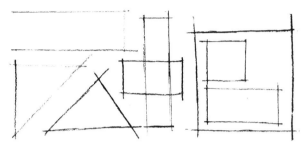

When you feel confident with these shapes, sketch circles inside the squares. Remember how you were told to draw circles on the previous page and you should find it quite easy. See how the circle touches the square in four places. It has no flats or points, it is a continuous curve. The same is true of an **ellipse**, a circle seen from an angle. It will fit into a rectangle.

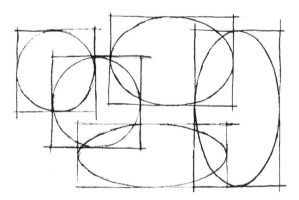

You now have all the shapes you need to draw some real things. Before you start to draw something, look at it carefully. Work out the basic shapes from which the object is made. A simple drinking mug starts as three rectangles. Draw the rectangles first. Make sure that they are in the right proportion. You can now complete the drawing by adding the curves.

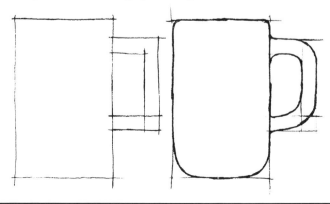

The next example is a good old-fashioned teapot, known as a Brown Betty. Can you see how it starts off as a square and a series of rectangles? Then the detail is gradually fitted in. If the rectangles are in the right proportion, the final drawing should be as well.

Good drawing relies on careful observation. When you draw something, try to forget what it is. Look at it as an arrangement of lines and curves. Then try to record them accurately.

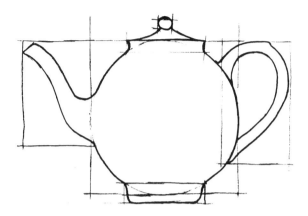

Activity 4 *Make a freehand drawing of a drinking mug or cup similar to the one shown here. Now alter the size of the rectangles and draw a series of mugs and cups. Some will probably appear ridiculous, but carry on. Do at least ten drawings, taking great care with each one. When you have finished, look at your drawings. Put a tick by those which you think would make good mugs or cups. Make a list of the design features which you think important in a mug or cup. Think about these words which all begin with S: SIZE, SAFETY, SHAPE, STRENGTH and SUITABILITY.*

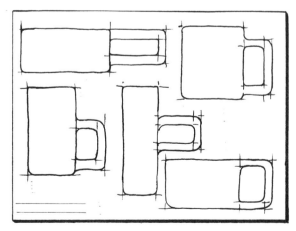

Activity 5 *Find an object with a spout that is used to pour, like a Brown Betty teapot. It could be another teapot, a jug or a watering can, for example. Make a drawing of it. Go through the stages shown with the teapot. Make a list of the design features of the object you have drawn.*

Applying shading

Line drawings will look more solid if **shading** is added. Shading shows the effect of light falling on an object and the way it is reflected. Shade is not the same as **shadow**.

Shade is found on the parts of the surface of an object which are not lit directly. Shadows are projected onto another surface by an object which shields the light from that surface.

When making design drawings, the shade is added following a convention. Always think of the light source as coming over your left shoulder. (This is because it is easier for the majority who are right-handed.) Follow this rule and you will quickly build up a visual memory of how simple objects appear when shaded. The simplest shading technique is a graded tone applied with a soft lead pencil.

Key points

- A 2B pencil is about right. You may prefer a slightly softer or harder pencil, depending on your results.
- The pencil needs to be sharp.
- Hold the pencil at an angle so that the full face of the lead is in contact with the paper.
- Move the pencil with horizontal strokes across the page.
- Density of shading can be varied in three ways.
  1 Vary the pressure you apply to the pencil.
  2 Build up density. Go over the shaded area until you have the darkness you want.
  3 Use different grades of pencil for different tones. This can be inconvenient.
- A drawing is shaded as if the light is coming over the left shoulder.
- Sharp edges and highlights can be made using a soft eraser.

Practise shading by trying out these key points. When you have the feel of what a pencil will do, try the following shading activities. You will quickly master this technique.

Activity 6 — **To draw and shade part of a view of a column** *Trace or copy onto your drawing paper the start of the top of the column given below. Continue the vertical lines for about 80 mm, using a straight edge. Make sure that the lines are parallel to each other.*

Decide on the tonal value of each face. Following the convention about light, the third face C will be in direct light and so will be lightest. Face G will be furthest from the light and so will be darkest. Face B will be slightly less dark than face A and so on. Before you start on the drawing, make a simple thumbnail sketch to determine the tones you will use for each face.

A	B	C	D	E	F	G

Now shade each face of the column, as you have decided. If you find difficulty in shading to an edge, use another piece of paper as a mask. Variations in tone can be smoothed in by smudging with your finger. Do this carefully and remember to keep your drawing and eraser clean.

When you are happy with your shading, add a capital to the pillar, as shown below. Work out how to shade it. The capital will cast a shadow on the column. Notice that the shadow is darker than the shading and has an even tone. Add the shadow and complete your drawing.

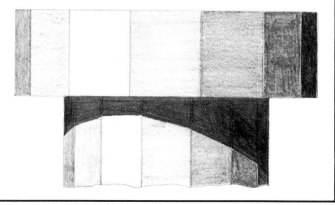

Some curved objects

You can turn simple two-dimensional line drawings into solid objects by adding shading. If you can draw rectangles, triangles and circles, you can also produce some good drawings.

A rectangle can become a cylinder. Notice how the lightest part is not in the centre but to the left-hand side. This is because the light is coming over your left shoulder, as with the column. The tone changes gradually, becoming darker where less light is being reflected.

A triangle can become a cone. Shading a cone is like shading a cylinder, except that the tonal values are triangular, tapering to the pointed end. If you find this difficult, start by making a quick thumbnail sketch of the tonal triangles as shown below.

A circle can become a sphere. Notice the position of the pool of light. The surface becomes darker as it curves away from this light spot. Shading strokes should follow the curve of the sphere. This makes it the most difficult of the three to shade well.

 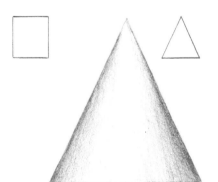 

There are other methods of giving form to a shape. Two are shown on the cylinders below. Try them for yourself. You will obtain better results using a pen or a fibre tip rather than a pencil.

Dots   You aim to increase dot density from the lightest part of the object to the darkest. An 0.35 mm pen or similar size fibre tip produces a good result. You can use this technique on spheres and cylinders.

Bar shading   You gradually increase the width of the bar from the lightest part of the object to the darkest. Leave a strip of light close to the edges. This increases the sense of roundness. You can treat cones in this way, but it is very difficult to bar shade spheres.

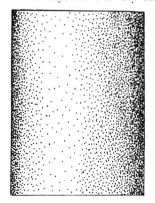 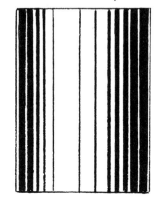

Activity 7   *Draw the outline of a space rocket, orbiting vehicle or any other type of space craft, to your own design. Shade the various shapes using one of the methods shown on this page. The space craft must be built from cylinders, cones and spheres. An example is given below.*

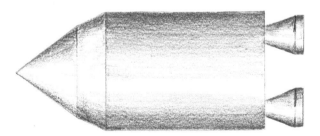

Activity 8   *This type of rendering is useful for giving form to line drawings of articles to be made on a lathe. Produce a design for **one** of the following and make a shaded design of your solution: a handle for a screwdriver, a chess piece or an egg cup.*

Objects which are circular in cross-section are known as **solids of revolution**.

ENLARGING AND REDUCING

To make a drawing larger or smaller is quite simple. We say that the drawing is being **scaled up** when we increase its size. We say that it is being **scaled down** when we decrease its size. There are several ways of doing this.

Using a grid   Place a grid over the original drawing. If you cannot draw directly onto the grid, draw a grid on tracing paper. Fix the traced grid over the drawing with masking tape. A better way is to scratch the grid onto clear film using a pin. The more accuracy you need, the finer you must make your grid.

Now draw a similar grid in the space in which the drawing must fit. It should have exactly the same number of squares. If you are enlarging the drawing, the squares must be bigger than the original ones. If you are reducing the drawing, they must be smaller.

Now transfer the original drawing onto the new squares, one square at a time. If you have a large grid, it might help you to label the lines. This should prevent you from making a mistake.

A **pantograph** is a simple mechanical device. It is used to rescale drawings either up or down. Later on you will learn how to make one. With practice they are quite easy to use.

Another method of enlarging a drawing is to use an **overhead projector**. Place a piece of clear acetate film over your original. (Tracing paper is no good.) Carefully scratch the outline onto the sheet with a needle or pin. Place the acetate with the drawing on it on the overhead projector. Project your drawing onto the wall to the size you want. Fix some paper to the wall and copy off your drawing. This method is very good for large drawings such as posters.

Activity 9   *Cut a copy of your favourite strip cartoon out of a paper or comic. Choose one funny section. Use the grid method to enlarge it to A4 size.*

DRAWING WITH SCISSORS

When you are looking for shapes, try cutting paper with scissors. It is a particularly useful way of searching for symmetrical shapes. Fold a piece of paper in half and cut out a shape. Open the paper out. You have a symmetrical shape with the fold in the centre. You can make a shape with identical quarters by folding the paper twice. Fold the paper one way, then the other. Scissors are also good for making curved shapes. It is often easier to get a smooth outline this way, than by drawing.

Activity 10   *Trace or copy the hairdryer body outline. Make some silhouette designs for a possible handle using scissors only. Start with some symmetrical shapes, then try some asymmetrical ones. Make them with coloured paper. Try six designs and lay them out as shown below. Comment by the side of each on how successful it would be.*

HANDLE

LETTERING

You will often need to add notes and headings to a drawing. They may provide extra information or explain an unclear drawing. This is called **annotating** a drawing. It is important that your lettering is tidy and looks good with your drawings. Poor lettering can spoil a design sheet. Develop your own style, but make sure it can be read. You will understand why this is important if you look at the examples below.

TRY USING CAPITAL LETTERS
KEEP YOUR LETTERING
NEAT AND EVEN
BE INDIVIDUAL

Can you read my handwriting.
Can you read my handwriting
Can you read My handwriting
Can you read My Handwriting !

Key points

- Use guidelines. Always start by drawing two feint parallel construction lines to keep your lettering even.
- Vary the width of your guidelines according to the importance of the information. Use a 4–5 mm width for notes on detail, 8–10 mm for subheadings and even more for page headings.
- A soft pencil will give you the best results. Start with an HB grade and then decide if you need a harder or softer pencil.
- For large lettering, it helps to add more construction lines, as shown here.
- Think carefully about headings. For example, using a shadow can make a title stand out from the page.

THE HEADING

THE HEADING

THE HEADING

Activity 11 Lettering can be fun. One way is to give **pictorial words** a visual quality. Look at the examples below. Try some pictorial words yourself. Start by drawing an accurate outline, then fit the letters in. Do a few roughs, then produce some finished drawings. Choose words/objects which will give you some scope. 'Ruler', for example, would be boring, but 'rocket', 'guitar', 'bridge' and 'shark' are possibilities. If you have problems with the outline, copy or trace the shape from a picture. You can add features to the word, like the bristles on the brush below. This increases the **graphic image**.

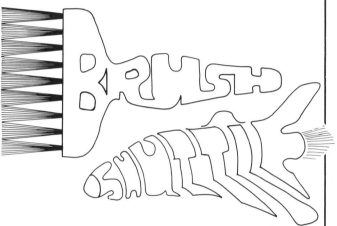

Activity 12 Try drawing some **suggestive words**. Make your drawing explain the meaning of the word. The letters may have to be distorted, expanded, condensed, curved, or angled. Construct a grid first to get the drawing right, as shown in the examples. Think of your own words, or try these: fat, thin, squash, fast, bulge, swell, shrink.

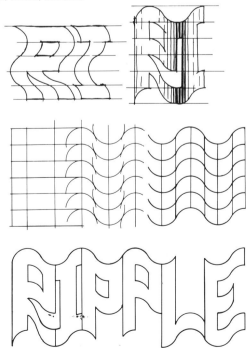

PLANS

A **plan** is a word with several uses. When we say a drawing is a plan, it means that it is a special type of view. Below are several examples of plan views. Look at them carefully. Can you work out what they have in common?

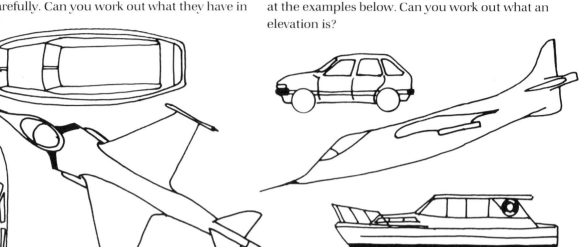

They are all views of objects seen from directly above. It is what we see if we look down on the top of a car, a boat, or an aeroplane. In a plan view, you can only see the length and the width. You cannot see the height. Here are two more plan views – an architect's plan of part of a house and a plan of part of a town (a map). In both cases symbols have been used to fit in all the detail.

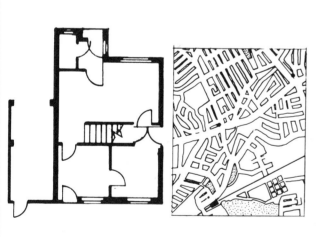

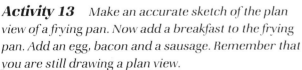

Activity 13   Make an accurate sketch of the plan view of a frying pan. Now add a breakfast to the frying pan. Add an egg, bacon and a sausage. Remember that you are still drawing a plan view.
Make a plan view of two of the following: kettle, chair, desk or sink. When you have completed them successfully, try two (more difficult) examples from this list: bicycle, sewing machine, smoothing plane, telephone.

ELEVATIONS

Elevation is the name given to another type of view. Like the plan views, elevations are two-dimensional. In any one view we can only see two dimensions. Look at the examples below. Can you work out what an elevation is?

To see the true shape of a surface we must look straight at it, or **square on**. An elevation is a view of the front, side or back of an object. If you look at the front or back, you will see the height and length. If you look at the side or end, you will see the height and width. Here are the elevations of a chair and a radio. Which two dimensions are shown in each view?

Activity 14   Use squared paper. Choose a building, such as your house or block of flats, part of your school, or a local church. Make accurate sketches of each of the elevations in turn. Check first that you can fit all the views on one sheet and all on the same base line. If your squared paper is A4 size, you may have to stick two pieces together.

Making solid drawings

It is important to be able to draw things quickly and accurately. It is very useful to be able to visualize a design, before you decide whether to make it. Solutions can be imagined in our 'mind's eye', but a drawing or model is necessary to check them out. The more closely the drawing resembles the imagined or actual appearance, the more helpful it will be.

So far you have mainly tried flat drawings. A flat drawing only shows two dimensions, for example height and width, or length and height. They appeared flat because they lacked depth. How can a feeling of depth be created on a flat sheet? There are several methods that can be used. Some of them are explained below. Put all the methods together and you will have a very convincing drawing.

PERSPECTIVE

This is the most important depth indicator. **Perspective** drawing follows rules which control the size and relative position of objects. These rules will be explained later. You may be able to work them out from the example below.

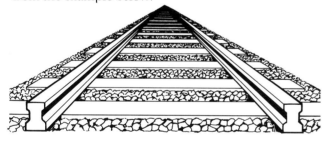

Size of familiar objects

Study the outline of the footballers. Which footballer is closest to you? Which is furthest away? Can you number them in order of distance from you? You did it easily because you expect footballers to be similar in size. If they appear smaller, they must be further away.

Overlap

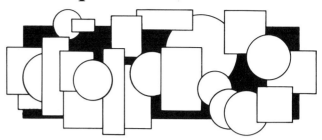

Look at the shapes. If one object or shape partly covers another one, we assume that it is the nearer of the two. Try to order the shapes shown. This is a strong clue to depth, because a shape obscures anything in line with it which is further away, unless it is transparent.

Shadow

Adding a shadow will often make a drawing of an object appear solid. A shadow shows the **direction** of the light source and its **intensity**.

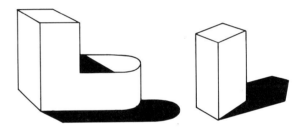

Texture

Texture or surface pattern helps to strengthen the sense of depth. Any regular or irregular texture will appear coarser, the closer it is to the viewing point.

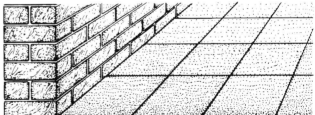

Did you know... *The rules of perspective were established in Italy during the fifteenth century. Two architects, Brunelleschi and Alberti, laid down the rules of a system often called **scientific perspective**. Greeks and Romans had realized the need for perspective, but had not really understood it. Other famous artists, such as Dürer and Leonardo da Vinci, invented machines to aid drawing in perspective. Later other devices, such as the camera obscura, were also used. Nowadays, the computer can produce perspective views of an object very quickly and the viewing point can be changed as wanted.*

The rules of perspective

You have already tried to work out the rules of perspective. How did you get on? It is possible to discover some of the rules from the drawing of the railway track.

- Parallel lines appear to get closer together as they go away from us. We say that they **converge** to a **vanishing point** where they disappear.
- Equal lengths appear smaller the further they are away. This is known as **foreshortening**.
- The surface closest to the viewing point is drawn to scale. All other heights, widths and lengths will foreshorten as they disappear into the distance or **recede**.

The drawing of the railway track obeys these rules. The parallel rails converge to a vanishing point. The equal length sleepers foreshorten as they recede. The true shape of the railway line is seen on the front surface. The shape of something that is cut through is called a **cross-section**.

The position of the vanishing point can be moved to give different views. Notice that the surface closest to the viewing point stays the same, wherever the vanishing point is.

The integrated circuit is drawn in two-point perspective. It has two vanishing points. The line joining the vanishing points is horizontal. It is known as the **horizon line**. The horizon line and the viewing point are on the same level and sometimes this is called **eye level**. The first two rules apply to two-point perspective. In addition there are two other rules.

- The vanishing points are positioned on a line known as the horizon line. It is always horizontal.
- The vertical edge closest to the viewing point is the only dimension drawn to scale. All other heights, widths and lengths will foreshorten as they recede.

By moving the object in relation to the viewing point, different views of the integrated circuit can be drawn. Three different types of views can be obtained.

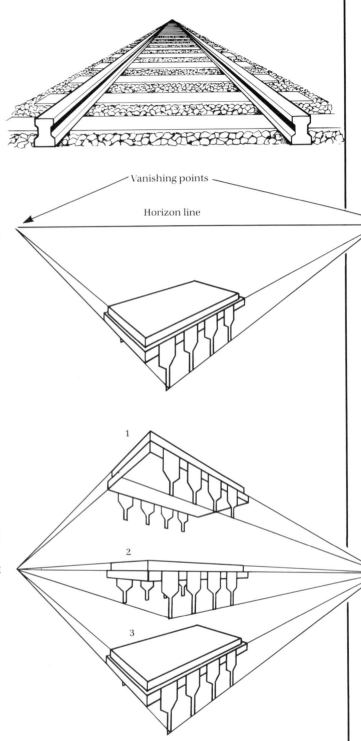

Vanishing points

Horizon line

1 When the object is above the horizon line, we see the underside of the object. This is often called a **worm's eye view**.
2 When the horizon line passes through the object, we see the **street level view**. (This is how we see buildings when we walk along a street.) Small objects drawn like this appear 'larger than life', because we associate this view with buildings and large things.

3 When the object is below the horizon line, we see the top of the object. We are looking down on it. This is often called a **bird's eye view**.

Whenever you wish to draw something in perspective, you must decide whether to use one or two-point perspective. You must also decide where to put the vanishing point and the horizon line, to give the best view of the object for your purpose.

Perspective sketching   Whenever you wish to draw or sketch an object, first you must draw a box into which it will fit. This is often called 'crating the object'. It helps you to get the proportions of the object correct – its height, width and length. It is worth practising sketching boxes. Here are some points to help you.

- Start with the front corner. Make sure it is vertical.
- Decide where the vanishing points will be. Sketch lines from the top and bottom of the vertical line to each vanishing point.
- Decide on the length and width of the box and complete the drawing.

Remember that you only need to worry about the direction of the line, as with drawing shapes. Its length will be fixed by the other lines. Attempt the next activities freehand. Do not use a straight edge. Freehand drawing is difficult, but the only way to improve is to practise.

Activity 15   Take an A3 sheet of paper and draw a horizon line across the middle. (Place the paper in the landscape position.) Fix the vanishing points and start sketching several boxes. Do not worry if they overlap. When you have the outline of several, decide which is the closest to you and draw the edges which you will see with a heavier line. Gradually work backwards, taking each box in turn. Line in only the parts of the boxes you will see. You will quickly give a feeling of depth to your drawing.

Line strength

When you are drawing an object, vary the strength of the lines to help to make it more solid. There are three types of lines. Use an ordinary line where you can see both surfaces which form the edge. Use a heavier line where you can only see one of the surfaces forming the edge. Use an even heavier line for the base line. This is where the object meets the surface on which it is sitting.

Activity 16   Practise drawing blocks. Use different strength lines to make them look more solid. When you have mastered a single block, draw four or five lying on a surface. Finally, sketch a simple tower which you could make with them.

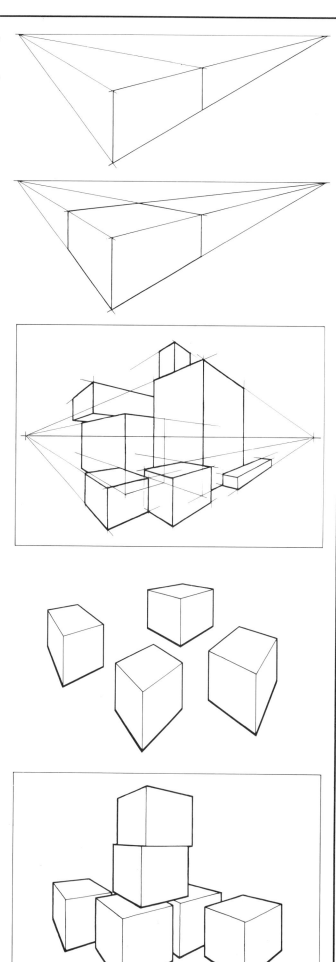

ESTIMATING DEPTHS IN PERSPECTIVE

A simple construction will help you to estimate depths in perspective. Start as always by sketching the box into which the object will fit. As an example we will divide this box into four units.

The next step is to draw the diagonal. Then divide the front edge into the number of units you require, in this case four. Join each of these divisions to the vanishing point.

Where each of these lines cuts the diagonal draw a vertical line and you will have four divisions. Notice how each unit is slightly smaller than the previous one, obeying the principles of perspective.

Another method of estimating depths is to start from a single cube and gradually add cubes until you obtain the size of object you require. Once you have drawn the first cube, draw a diagonal across its face. Then draw another diagonal parallel to the first as shown. Where it crosses the line to the vanishing point you have the corner of the next cube and so on.

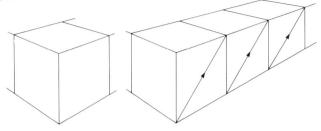

You can build up as big a block as you require, increasing the height as well if you wish. It is also possible to subdivide units. See if you can work out how to do it. Using these methods you can produce a perspective grid. If you draw a grid it can be used as an underlay to help the accuracy of your drawing.

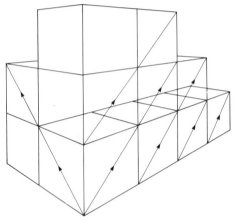

Activity 17 *Sketch in two-point perspective, two times life size, a match box with the drawer two-thirds out. You must start off by deciding which type of perspective to use. Make sure you get the outline correct, then you can start to add more details, such as matches. Try to make the drawing as realistic as possible.*

DRAWING CIRCLES IN PERSPECTIVE

In two-point perspective circles will appear as ellipses. This is because you are viewing the object at an angle and foreshortening is taking place. If you hold a coke can in your hand end on it appears as a circle. Turn it slowly away from you and it will eventually become a straight line. All the shapes in between are ellipses.

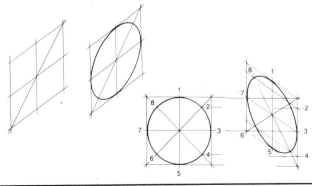

To draw a circle in perspective start by sketching the square into which it will fit. Next find the mid-points. The circle will pass through the four marked points. The curve must be sketched in freehand. Your first result may not be very good, but you will quickly improve.

To produce a more accurate circle you need to find more points. The construction here shows you how to do this.

Activity 18 *Find something roughly cylindrical in shape such as a transistor, cotton reel, lipstick or coke can and make a two-point perspective sketch of it. You may have to scale the drawing up or down depending on what you choose. Try to produce a drawing which will fit onto an A4 sheet. Remember, outline first then make your drawing realistic by adding detail.*

SOLID LETTERS

Now you have started to master drawing simple solid objects, you can move on to something more complicated. So that it is not too difficult, it is a good idea to start with shapes that you are familiar with, such as letters. When we write, the words are usually two-dimensional, as they are made up of a single line. To complete drawings of solid letters you must imagine that the letters are three-dimensional – a bit like the chocolate letters you can buy in the shops just before Easter.

Activity 19 On this page you will be shown, stage by stage, three ways in which you might sketch a letter A. Study the stages carefully and then use your imagination to draw some solid letters. You could try to produce a complete alphabet of solid letters. Draw each letter in rough first. When you are satisfied that it is correct, transfer it to your finished drawing using one of the methods explained earlier.

First sketch a box in perspective which will contain the letter. It should have the same overall height, width and length as the letter you are going to draw. Remember the box will have two vanishing points and all your horizontal lines will appear to be passing through one or other of these two points.

The next step is to sketch the detail of the letter on one of the faces of the box you have already drawn. The examples show how an A might look on each face. Take care to draw each part of the letter accurately.

The letter can be completed by giving it thickness, width or depth. Now you can see the solid letter. The drawing may need adjusting or changing. It is very difficult to get it right first time.

When a reasonable sketch has been achieved it can be transferred to the final sheet. This also allows the finished word or alphabet to be carefully laid out. The outline letters look quite solid, but you will be able to make them appear more realistic by adding shade and shadow. You will learn how to do this in the next few pages. Then you can complete your alphabet.

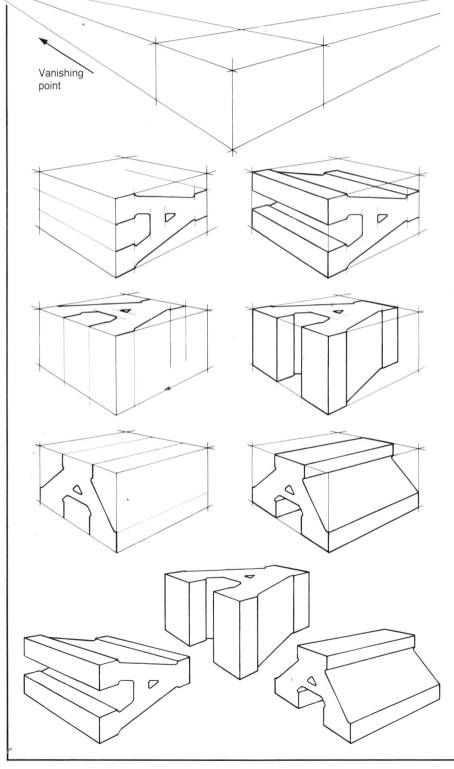

Vanishing point

SHADING PERSPECTIVE VIEWS

The next step in making your drawing look more realistic is to add some shading. You can build on the principles you have already mastered. How will the basic forms appear when light falls on them? Start with the **cube**.

Key points

- A drawing of a cube has three faces. Each will reflect a different amount of light, so each face will be shaded in a different tone.
- The light is coming from over your left shoulder.
- The top surface will be the lightest, the left-hand face the next lightest (a medium tone) and the right-hand face the darkest.

The next group are all **prisms**. A prism is a solid which has the same cross-section all along its length. Most pencils, for example, are hexagonal prisms. Notice how each one is shaded. The faces become darker as they turn away from the light.

A **pyramid** is like a prism except that the sides narrow to the **apex** or point.

Perspective **cylinders** and **cones** are very similar to the simple ones you have already drawn. In a solid sketch, however, you can see either the top or the bottom. Notice on the tube the position of the lightest area of the internal surface.

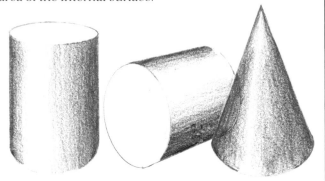

The sphere is exactly the same as the one on page 15. The outline of a sphere will appear as a circle in every type of drawing.

Activity 20

1   *Copy or trace the outline of a child's pull-along toy. It is made up of very simple shapes. Once you have a good copy, shade it. A thumbnail sketch is given for guidance.*

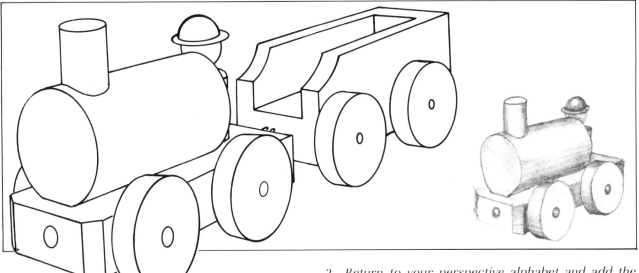

2   *Return to your perspective alphabet and add the shading to the letters you have already drawn.*

ADDING THE SHADOW

Shadows are important visual clues in a drawing. They help you to make your drawings more realistic. Remember that a shadow is the projection onto another surface of an object which is shielding that surface from the light. Shadows can be cast by any light source, for example the sun, a light bulb, or a candle. You will start adding shadows as if the light is coming from the sun. The sun's rays can be considered to be parallel. This makes the drawing much more straightforward.

Key points

- The shadow will have a shape similar to the object. It may be distorted.
- The light source fixes the position of the shadow.
- The shadow is generally darker than the darkest tone on the drawing.
- Parts of an object can cast shadows on other parts of the same object.

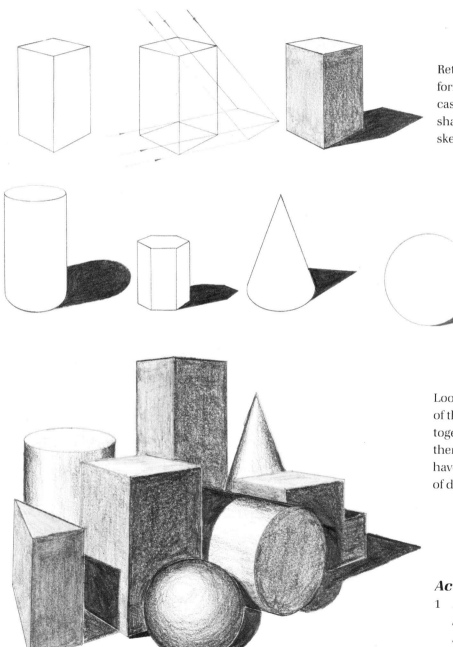

Return to the basic geometric forms and see what shadows they cast. If you remember these shapes, you can add them to your sketches.

Look what happens when several of the simple blocks are put together. First add the shading, then the shadow and you soon have a solid drawing with a feeling of depth.

Activity 21

1 *Return to Activity 16 on page 21. Shade the tower you sketched and add a shadow.*
2 *Add the shadow to the pull-along toy drawn on the previous page.*

TEXTURE

The objects you have drawn so far have all been made from a material such as wood, metal or plastic. You have not shown which material in your drawing. This is done by adding **texture**.

Texture is the look or feel of a surface. You can recognize most materials by feeling them. Your fingers are as familiar with the touch and feel as your eyes are with the appearance. When drawing a material you can use visual clues to show its texture. Look at the examples here. They will provide guidance. Apply the rules of shading to texture: most light least texture, least light most texture.

Wood   This material has a distinctive **grain** pattern on its surface. You can use simple lines to show the pattern. There are different types of grain. If you are in doubt, get a block of wood and look carefully at the grain. Copy what you see.

Metal   Many different types of surface finish are found on metal. If the metal has been cast in sand, the surface has a texture similar to sand. Use a simple **stippling** technique. If the metal has been extruded, use **form shading**. Vary the distance between the parallel lines according to the light falling on the surface. For a polished surface use **bar shading**. The bars must follow the form of the object.

Plastic   As with metal, there are many surface finishes. The most common is a highly polished reflective surface. You will normally wish to show the colour of a plastic object. Some guidelines on how to do this are given later. Beware – plastic is often used to look like other materials, such as wood and leather. It is also often given a geometric texture or pattern to make it easier to grip.

Rubber   Rubber is a smooth but dull material. Use slightly heavier stippling than on cast metal. As with plastic, textures are often moulded on the surface for specific reasons.

Concrete   The texture of concrete reflects its composition. On the surface you see evidence of sand, ballast and maybe the material into which it was cast. This is usually wood of some variety.

Glass   Glass is **transparent**. You can see through it to the object on the other side. All you see is some sign of the surface reflection.

Your drawings will be more successful if you spend

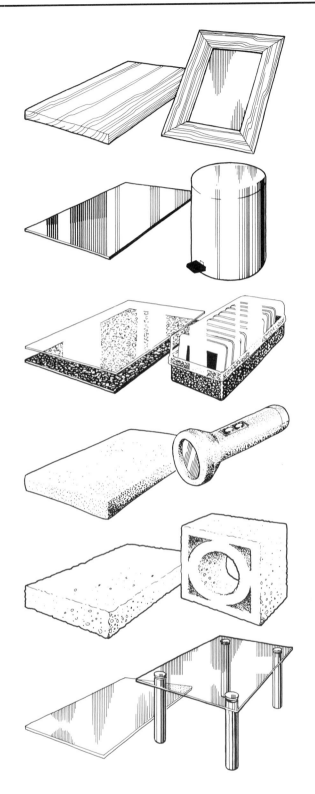

time looking at objects made from the various materials and drawing them. Accurate observation is the key to successful drawing.

Activity 22   *Trace the outline of five or six of your perspective letters. Make the letters appear as if they are made of a specific material. Use the textures illustrated on this page. If you have time, and for fun, trace some more outlines and make the letters appear to be made from cheese, rock, cake, brick, foam, or any other material you can draw.*

A RENDERED DRAWING

You are now ready to draw an actual object. Follow stage by stage the way in which a drawing is gradually built up to make a finished **rendered** view.

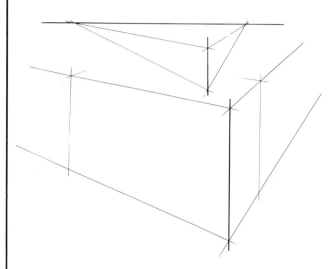

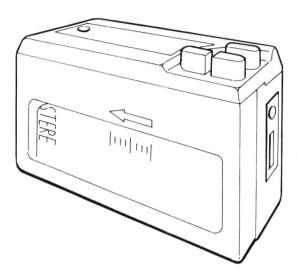

Stage 1   Examine the object and decide upon the basic forms that make it up. Establish the perspective boxes into which they fit. Make sure the proportions are right before you proceed.

Stage 3   Confirm the outline and begin to add the detail. Make sure that you continue to use the two vanishing points and that the foreshortening looks accurate.

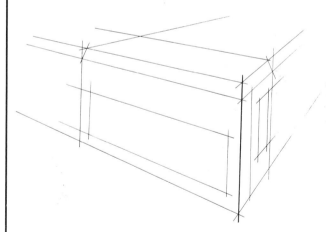

Stage 2   Sketch in the outline of the forms. You can now begin to see the drawing taking shape.

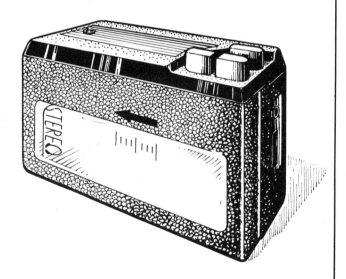

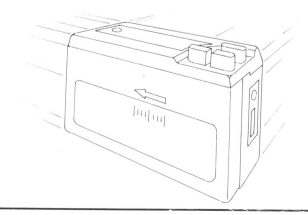

Stage 4   Transfer the outline to a fresh sheet. Start to shade the drawing and to show texture where appropriate. Add the shadow, both on the object and on the surface on which it is resting.

Activity 23   *Find a man-made object which is held in the hand. A torch, an electric shaver or a portable radio will do, or any object about the same size as a calculator. Make a rendered sketch of the object by following the four stages above.*

Technical graphics

BASIC DRAWING AIDS

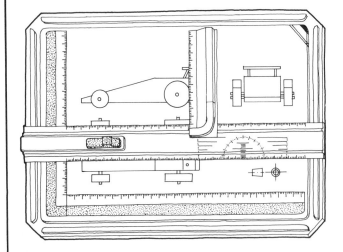

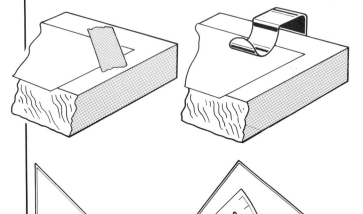

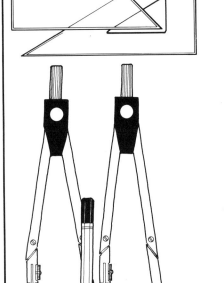

Drawing boards

So far, all you have needed is a flat surface to draw on. Now you will need a **drawing board** with the means for drawing parallel lines.

The simplest type is a board with a flat surface and a straight edge. A **T square** against the edge is used to make parallel lines. This is quite adequate if it is carefully looked after. The drawing studio in which you work at school may have boards with **parallel motions**. You can slide the parallel motion up and down the board; it always stays parallel to the top and bottom edges. If you use a wooden board hold your paper securely in place with **masking tape** or **spring clips**.

Many people prefer **draughting palettes**, as shown here. They have many advantages: the groove in the edge allows lines to be drawn parallel to any edge; there is a clamp on the edge for holding the paper; they are lighter than traditional boards; they are far less likely to become inaccurate with use. The edge of the board and the parallel straight edge have millimetre scales on them. This means a separate ruler is not needed.

Set squares

You also need to be able to draw lines at certain angles. **Set squares** give you angles at 30, 45, 60 and 90 degrees. An **adjustable square** allows you to draw a line at any angle. It can also be used to measure angles, but a protractor is probably easier to use.

Drawing circles

There are many instruments for drawing circles. There are, for example, three main types of compass: bow, divider and beam. **Bow compasses** generally have a spring and are adjusted by a screwthread. They are very accurate. You can get them in many sizes and they are especially useful for drawing small circles. **Divider compasses** have a friction or a geared joint. They are less accurate than springbows, but they are good for larger circles. Divider compasses are also useful for stepping off equal distances. **Beam compasses** are used for very large circles.

Most compasses can be used with pencils or technical pens. If you wish to draw a circle with a felt tip, or something which will not fit into your compass, tape the pen to the compass.

Measuring aids

An accurate ruler is essential. If you are lucky enough to have a drawing palette, you will not need a ruler as well. Many drawings need to be done to a certain scale. You can use special rulers known as **scales**. Scales let you reduce or enlarge measurements without any calculation. They are useful for making drawings and for reading measurements from them.

The three most common shapes of scales are shown below. The **bevel edge** is the most usual and can be used for most things. The **four bevel** or **slimline** lets you measure dimensions to the highest degree of accuracy. The **triangular** has up to 12 different scales on its six edges.

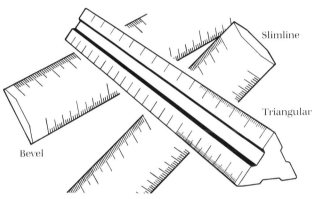

Slimline

Triangular

Bevel

Drawing aids

Plastic **templates** are available to draw any geometric shape or symbol you need. They are expensive and very few are really essential. You may find useful some of these:

French curves   Sets of eight pieces or less which give you a wide range of shapes.
Radius curves and **circle templates**   These are useful for drawing arcs of a circle or complete circles. The radius curve is a positive shape and the circle template is a negative shape.

Ellipse templates   There are many of these. They are very useful but you will need a lot to cover all the ellipses you might draw.
Symbol templates   These templates have the symbols used on architectural, electronic and engineering drawings.

Another useful aid is a **flexible** or **flexi curve**. It is a bit like a lead snake! It can be bent to any curved shape and then used as a drawing aid.

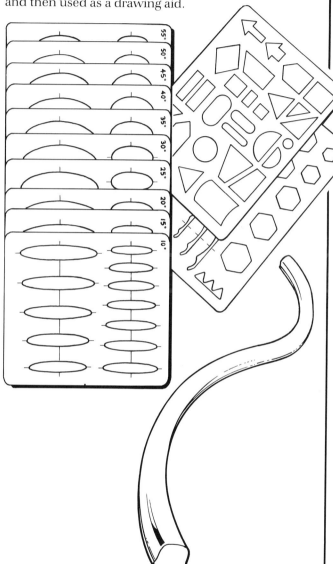

Key points

- Keep your instruments clean. Wipe them occasionally with a little methylated spirit or lighter fuel.
- Use a slightly softer lead in your compass than the pencil you use for drawing.
- Sharpen the compass lead to a chamfer on a glass paper block.
- Use templates etc. with a stepped edge if you are using ink or felt tip. This stops the ink from running underneath. If your templates do not have a stepped edge, use one on top of another.
- Look after your instruments carefully. The accuracy of your drawing depends on them.

ESSENTIAL CONSTRUCTIONS

Practise with your drawing instruments by mastering these constructions. You will find them useful in the drawing studio and whenever you wish to mark something out accurately.

Dividing lines and angles

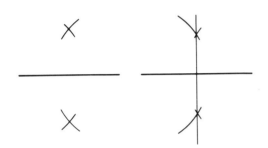

Bisect a line   Set your compass to at least half the length of the line. Strike an arc above and below the line from both ends. Join the points where the two arcs cross. The line you have just drawn divides the original line in half and is at 90 degrees to it.

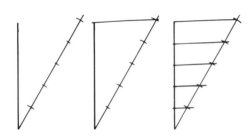

Divide an angle into equal parts   Draw any line at an angle to the original one. Step off along this line the number of divisions you want. Join the last point to the end of the line. Draw lines parallel to this line from each of the points. These parallel lines will divide the original line into the number of equal parts that you wanted.

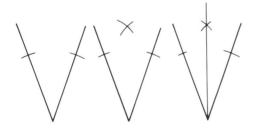

Bisect an angle   Mark equal distances from the apex along each line making the angle. Set your compass to any radius and draw arcs from these two points. Draw a line from the apex to where the two arcs cross. This line bisects the angle.

Constructing shapes

Regular polygons   These are shapes with any number of sides which are equal in length. The angles between the sides are also equal.

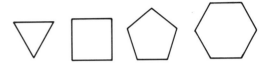

- Bisect the initial side of the regular polygon.
- From one end of the line draw an angle of 45 degrees and an angle of 60 degrees.
- Label the point where the 45 degree angle crosses the bisector of the side '4'. Label the point where the 60 degree angle crosses the bisector '6'.

- Bisect the line between 4 and 6. Label this point '5'. Set your compass to the distance between 5 and 6.
- Now mark point 7, beyond point 6, with your compass. Then mark 8 beyond 7, and so on.

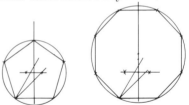

- The numbered points are the centres of **circumscribing circles** of regular polygons having that number of sides. ('Circumscribing' means a circle that goes round the shape, just touching each corner.)
- Draw the circumscribing circle. Step off around the circle, using your compass set to the length of the side.
- Join these points and you have the regular polygon you wanted.

Activity 24   *Work out these simple fractions to one decimal place, using one of the constructions above: $\frac{7}{6}$, $\frac{13}{11}$ and $\frac{5}{7}$. Check your answer with your calculator. How accurate were your constructions?*

Activity 25   *Draw a regular heptagon (7 sides) and a regular dodecagon (12 sides). This requires great accuracy. Can you work out how to turn them into coins? Find out the names of all the other regular polygons.*

Circles in contact externally

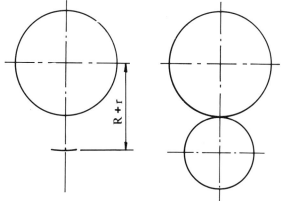

Two circles Draw Circle 1. Set your compass to the sum of the radii of the two circles. With your compass set to this distance, draw an arc from the centre of Circle 1. The centre of Circle 2 can lie anywhere on this arc.

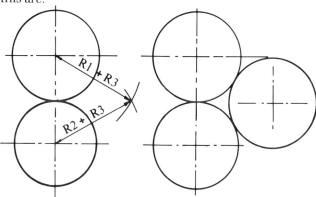

Three circles Draw Circles 1 and 2 in contact, as above. Set your compass to the sum of the radii of Circle 1 and Circle 3, which you have not yet drawn. With your compass set to this distance, draw an arc from the centre of Circle 1. Set your compass to the sum of the radii of Circle 2 and Circle 3, which you still have not yet drawn. With your compass set to this distance, draw an arc from the centre of Circle 2. The centre of Circle 3 is where the two arcs cross. There are two possible positions.

Circles in contact internally

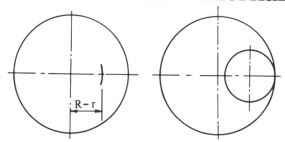

Two circles Draw the larger of the two circles. Set your compass to the radius of the larger circle minus the radius of the smaller circle. With your compass set to this distance, draw an arc from the centre of the larger circle. The centre of the smaller circle can lie anywhere on this arc.

Activity 26 *Copy the drawing of the telephone receiver. Draw it as carefully as you can, finding the exact centres of the circles as shown.*

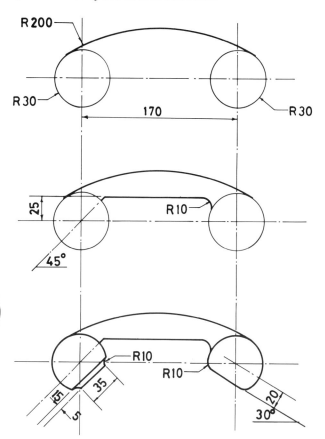

The surfaces of the mouthpiece and the earpiece might be called **functional surfaces**. *Their relative positions are based on considerable research and the average size of people's hands and heads. Design your own handpiece without altering their relative positions. It must be comfortable to hold, so make this a design factor as well. Sketch the shapes within a rectangle, with the two functional surfaces in the correct positions. Make four or five designs, then choose the best one. Transfer the shape to a piece of card, cut it out and see how well it works. Make notes on your design sheet about the success or otherwise of your solution.*

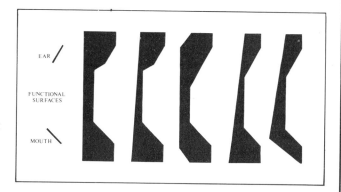

TESSELLATION

A pattern of shapes which covers a surface leaving no gaps is called a **tessellation**. The individual shapes are called **tesserae**. The simplest tessera is a square like tiles in a bathroom or kitchen. They tessellate across the surface, covering it completely. Bricks in a wall, tiles on a roof, patterns on fabric or wallpaper are all examples of tessellating patterns. Look at the examples of differently shaped tiles which have been used as pavements in shopping centres. Can you spot other shapes which tessellate across a surface?

Tessellating shapes can be made from basic geometric shapes, such as a square or an equilateral triangle. These simple shapes can be arranged in different ways to give a surface more interest.

Squares

You can make tiles from squares, using grids. The square can be used as the basic unit, or it can be subdivided into subunits. By using a grid, you will quickly find shapes which will make tiles. Sometimes, two shapes will be needed to fill a surface completely. Follow carefully the three examples shown. Make sure that you can see how the basic shape makes up each one.

Did you know... *Representational art (drawing real objects) is not as important in Islamic culture as it has been in Christian culture. Islamic art is based on geometry and the development of abstract decoration. Islamic artists produce the finest examples of repeating units, or tessellating patterns, using only compass and rule. These patterns are often in the form of tiles. They are used to decorate the walls of buildings, both inside and out. The floors are often also tiled, or the patterns are reproduced on carpets.*

Equilateral triangles

One of the pavement examples is based on an equilateral triangle. Six equilateral triangles make a hexagon – another shape which tessellates perfectly on a surface. Can you think of some examples of hexagons tessellating? You can easily draw a hexagon with a compass. Tiles can be based on the equilateral triangle or the hexagon. Both tessellate on a surface, so subunits based on these shapes will also tessellate. The subunits may form the tile, or they may be joined to shapes in other units forming larger tiles. Two shapes may be made which will jointly tessellate over the surface. Follow carefully the three examples which show how tiles can be designed.

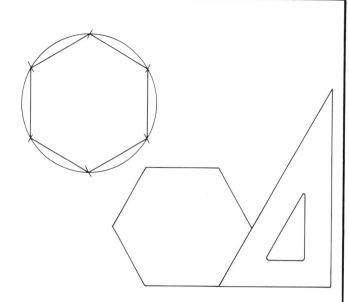

Activity 27 *Copy carefully at least two of the tile patterns shown on these two pages. You will need to use constructions you have already learnt. Accurate drawing is essential. Use coloured pencils to show up each tile, or cut the tiles out of coloured paper and glue them down carefully.*

Design a tile based on equilateral triangles and hexagons or squares. Make these tiles out of card, to show how they will tessellate across a surface.

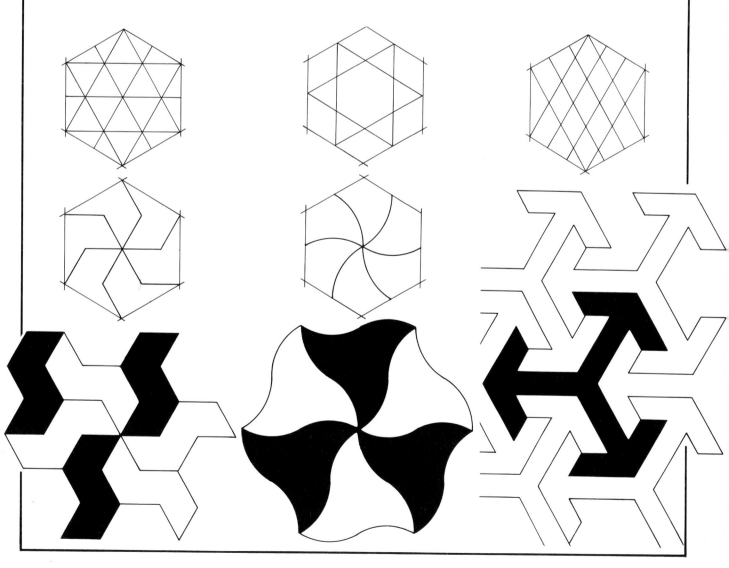

PATTERN

Pattern has several meanings. There are two important uses of the word. A pattern can be a set of working instructions – a pattern for a dress, for example. A pattern can also describe surface decoration – the pattern of a carpet or wallpaper, for example. Tiles form patterns, but each tile may also have a pattern on it. There are many ways you can make patterns. The ones explained here are **geometrical** patterns. Later you will develop patterns based on natural forms.

Using templates

Start by designing a single unit which can be repeated. Make a paper or card template. Remember that you can fold the paper to make the shape if it is symmetrical. Try using your template between two parallel lines. Create several arrangements. Next work in squares. Produce four squares with the pattern, then arrange the squares in different ways. There are hundreds of ways you can use your single unit to make many patterns.

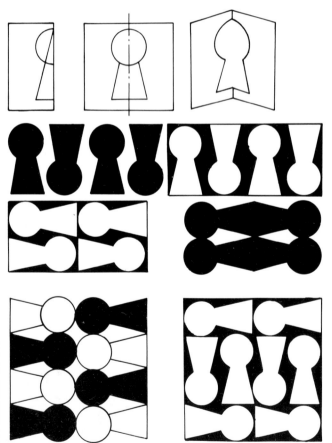

Radial patterns

These patterns are based on geometrical construction. You can make them using compasses and basic instruments. Sometimes they are called **tracery** patterns, because they look like the windows in cathedrals and some large churches. You can also make these patterns by folding the paper several times before cutting it. The number of folds fixes the number of times each cut shape is repeated.

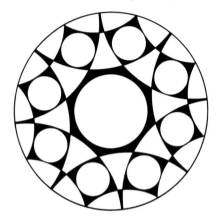

Interlocking and woven patterns

These patterns look like a material that is interlocking or woven. You can draw a strip so that it appears to go under or over another strip. It is easy to do, as in this simple doodle. If you do it in a regular way, you can make a pattern.

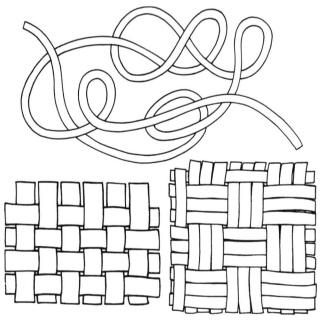

Activity 28   *Try out each of the techniques shown on this page. Produce some examples of different patterns. Use coloured pencils to make the pattern stand out.*

THE ELLIPSE

The ellipse is another important geometric shape. Unfortunately, there is no instrument like a compass which will draw any size ellipse. Templates may help you, but it is useful to know how to draw any size ellipse. Here are two methods.

1 Auxiliary circle

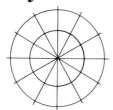

- Draw two circles, one with the radius of the major axis and the other with the radius of the minor axis.
- Draw a series of diagonals.

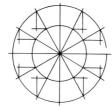

- Where each diagonal crosses the smaller circle, draw a horizontal line.
- Where each diagonal crosses the larger circle, draw a vertical line.

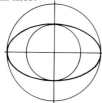

- The horizontal and vertical lines from each diagonal cross at a point on the circumference of the ellipse.
- Join these points with a freehand curve.

2 Trammel method

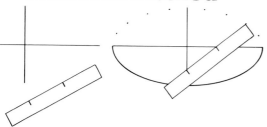

- Draw the major and minor axes of the ellipse.
- Take a strip of paper and from one end measure and mark half the major and half the minor axis.
- Use the trammel as shown to find points on the circumference of the ellipse.
- Join these points with a freehand curve.

Activity 29 *The trademark of an international petrol company, ESSO, is bordered by an ellipse. Draw the border of the trademark to the given sizes. Use one method for the outer ellipse and the other method for the inner ellipse. ESSO was originally called Standard Oil of New Jersey. It was founded by John D. Rockefeller, a multi-millionaire. There were many companies with the initials SO and this caused confusion. To overcome this ES was put in front of SO. The resulting **phonetic name** ESSO sounded the same as before. In America the company had to change its name again. It is known there as EXXON. This name was one of 10 000 words which were produced by a computer. EXXON was chosen after extensive research.*

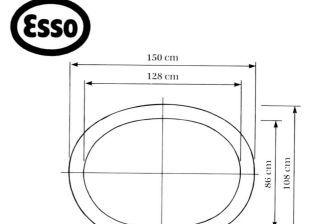

You can make a phonetic name for a company using the initial letter of your name. My name is Richard, so the first letter of my name is R. Spelt phonetically this is AR. If I now add CO, the short form for company, I get the name ARCO. If I use the initial letter of my surname in the same way, I invent the name TECO. I can use both letters and make the name ARTECO. Make a name for a company with your initials. Now place your name inside the ellipse border, making sure that the letters are clear, distinct and can be easily read.

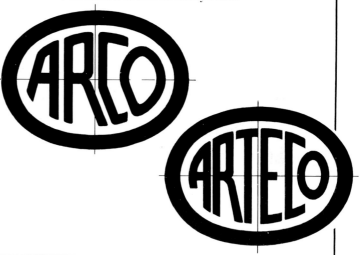

Drawing systems

You can read and understand this book because you and I speak the same language – English. Different languages are used in drawing. They are called **systems** or **projections**. In this chapter, you will learn about some of the common drawing systems. The language or system you use will let you communicate, through drawings, with other people who understand the same system. These views of a staple gun are arranged randomly, making them difficult to understand.

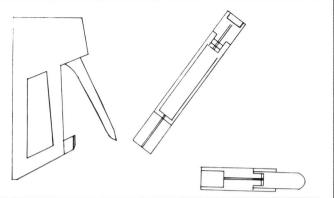

ORTHOGRAPHIC PROJECTION

This is a very important drawing system. All the information about an object can be shown on this type of drawing. You need orthographic views to make things. This is the only system which shows all the detail. The staple gun, redrawn in orthographic projection, can now be understood.

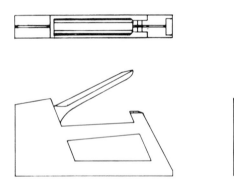

Orthographic projection is a method of relating plans and elevations. You draw each face of an object separately. You position these views in a special way. Anyone who understands orthographic projection uses these views to build up a mental image of what the object looks like. This may seem difficult at first. With practice you should master the technique.

There are two types of orthographic projection, **first angle** and **third angle**.

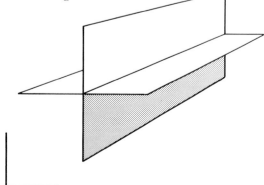

Orthographic projections are drawn in relation to two surfaces, the horizontal plane and the vertical plane. These are flat surfaces which intersect at right angles, because one is vertical and the other is horizontal. These planes divide space into four parts or **quadrants**. These are known as the first, second, third and fourth angles.

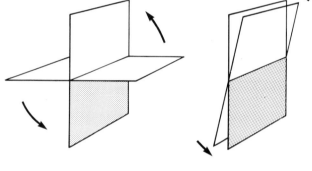

The horizontal plane is rotated as shown to make these planes flat. This means that they can be drawn on a piece of paper.

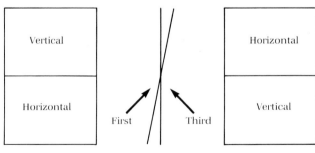

The first angle is now opened out on the front of the piece of paper and the third angle on the back. The second and fourth angles have disappeared. If you are uncertain, make a model with two pieces of paper and see what happens.

Notice the difference. In first angle, the vertical plane (VP) is at the top of the page and the horizontal plane (HP) is at the bottom. The line where they intersect is called the XY line. In third angle, the VP is at the bottom half of the page and the HP is at the top.

First angle

A small wooden toy has been placed in the first angle. Let us see how to get orthographic views of this toy.

Lines are projected back from the toy onto the planes (like shadows, except that all the detail of the object can be seen). The view on the vertical plane is an elevation (seen from the side). The view on the horizontal plane is the plan (seen from above).

Take the toy away, fold out the planes and there are the views in first angle orthographic projection. This elevation is called the **front elevation**.

Two views are not enough to show all the detail. The vertical plane can be bent at right angles to give two more elevations. These are called **end elevations**. One end elevation is sometimes all you will need. This will give the complete first angle orthographic projection of the toy.

Key points

In first angle orthographic projection:

- The elevations are above the XY line.
- The plan view is below the XY line.
- The left-hand end of the object is seen in the end elevation to the right of the front elevation.
- The right-hand end of the object is seen in the end elevation to the left of the front elevation.
- The front elevation is the most important elevation and is always positioned directly above the plan.

Did you know... *The prefix 'ortho-' means straight, rectangular, upright, correct. An orthographic drawing is, therefore, one which is straight, rectangular and correct. Drawings of this type were made during the Renaissance in fourteenth and fifteenth century Italy. Only at the beginning of the eighteenth century were they formalized into the system shown here. A French military engineer, Gaspard Mange, was responsible. His method of projecting orthographic views was a military secret to start with. It soon became the common language of engineers throughout Europe. This system allowed complex machines to be designed and drawn accurately. Drawings would have been hopelessly confused without the orthographic system.*

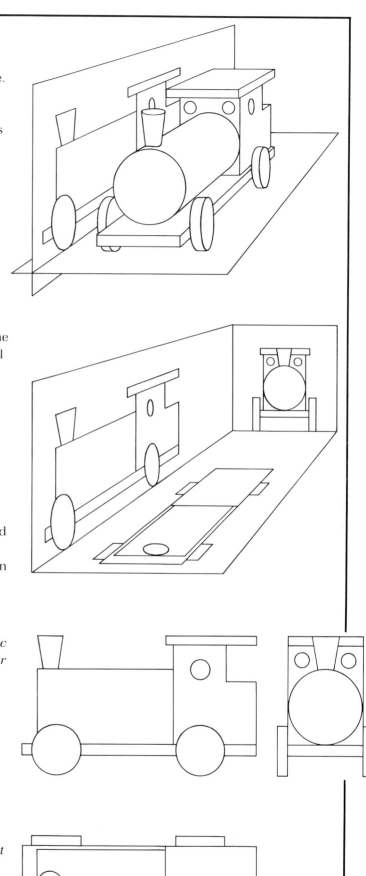

Third angle

Imagine that the HP and the VP are made out of glass. Through the planes you can see the wooden toy. It is now in the third angle.

Lines are projected from the toy onto the planes. In third angle, these lines are forward towards our viewing point, rather than away from it as in first angle. The views have the same names.

Take the toy away, flatten out the planes and there are the views of the toy in third angle orthographic projection. The plan view will come above the front elevation, because the HP rotates upwards.

As in first angle, further elevations can be added by bending the vertical plane. The view of the right-hand end appears on the right side of the front elevation.

Here is the complete third angle orthographic projection of the toy.

Key points

In third angle orthographic projection:

- The elevations lie in a horizontal line and are below the XY line.
- The plan view is above the XY line.
- The left-hand end of the object is seen in the end elevation to the left of the front elevation.
- The right-hand end of the object is seen in the end elevation to the right of the front elevation.
- The front elevation is the most important elevation and is always positioned directly below the plan.

You must always state which projection your orthographic drawing is in. Use these symbols to distinguish between first and third angle.

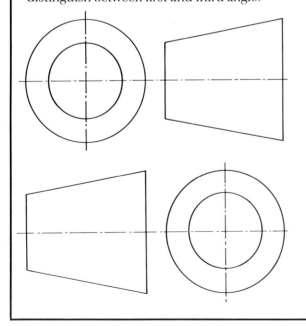

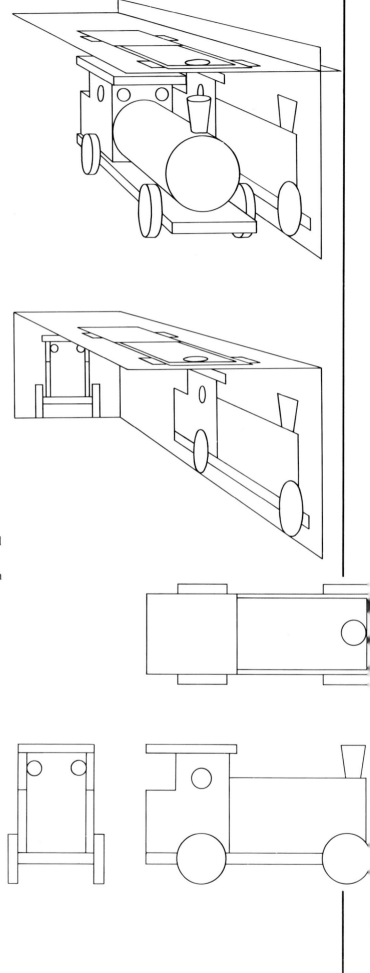

Activity 30 Use squared paper for this activity. Here are five incomplete orthographic views of common objects. Copy the views here and then add a third view. Start by checking whether the drawing is first or third angle. Add more detail to your completed views.

Activity 31 Use squared paper for this activity. Here are the simplified outline sketches of some common objects. Draw orthographic views of each object. Do any three in first angle and the remaining two in third angle. Add the correct symbol to show which angle you have used.

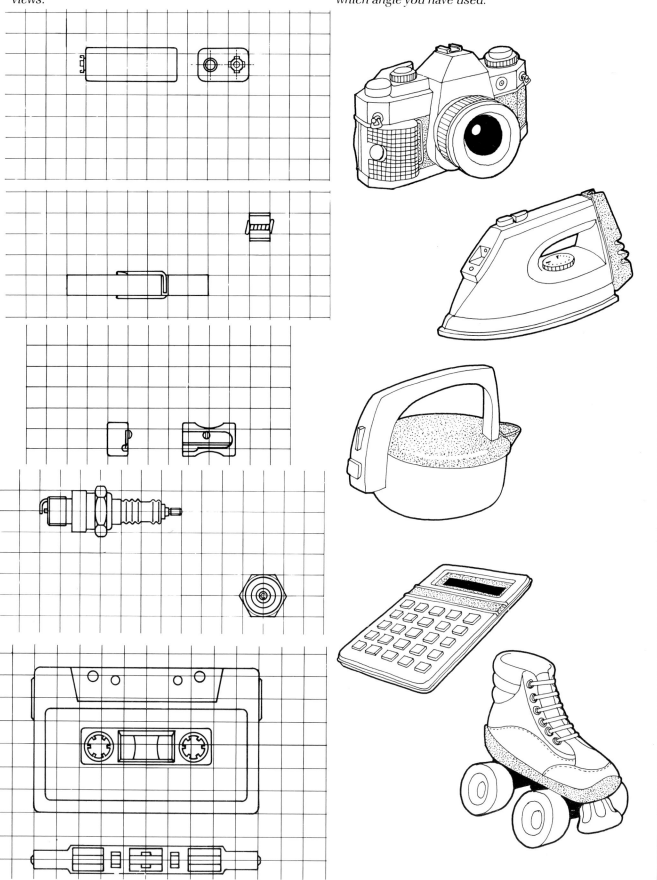

Making an orthographic drawing

These are the stages in making an orthographic drawing. We shall use the toy train as the example, as you are familiar with it. Draw all horizontal lines with a T square or parallel motion. Draw vertical lines with a set square resting on the parallel motion.

Decide if you will draw in first or third angle. This drawing is in third angle. How large is the object? Its size fixes the scale of the drawing. The drawing was done on an A3 sheet of paper full size. The drawings have been reduced to fit them into the book.

Do a thumbnail sketch of the views you will draw. Work out the sizes and positions on the page of the boxes into which each view will fit.

Your first lines on the final sheet are construction lines. Draw these lightly with a hard pencil like a 4H. First draw in the projection lines, between which the plan and front elevation will be drawn. Complete the box for the plan and front elevation. Continue the lines which give the height of the front elevation and the width of the plan across the page.

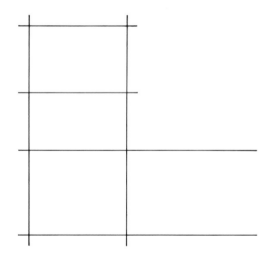

Draw a line at 45 degrees from the front elevation as shown. This line is used to project the width of the

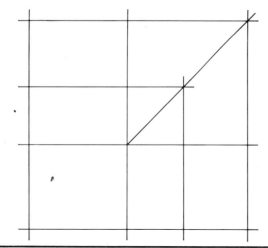

object from the plan view. This gives the box into which the end elevation will fit. The position of the three views is now fixed.

Show the centres of all circles, curved and symmetrical objects with a **centre line**. A centre line is a thin chain line. Once you have the centres, draw in all the full circles using a compass. Remember that your compass should have an HB lead. Do not draw any parts of circles, such as for the driver's hat, until the lines which fix their size have been drawn.

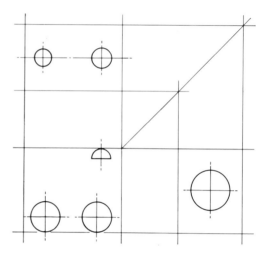

Now add the rest of the detail. It is a good habit to transfer dimensions from one view to another, using your instruments rather than measuring. This will help to make your drawings more accurate.

Draw in the outline with a 2H pencil. Make sure that corners meet and do not cross. Do not press heavily.

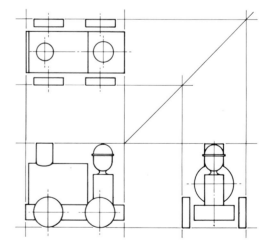

Important detail often cannot be seen, because it is hidden inside or behind another part of the object. In this drawing you cannot see the depth of the hole in which the man is standing. You can show such detail using dotted lines. Draw these short dash lines with a 4H pencil.

ADDING DIMENSIONS

If someone is going to make the object you have drawn, dimensions will be needed. There are right and wrong ways of **dimensioning** a drawing. The drawing of the toy has been dimensioned according to these rules. The dimensions do not dominate the drawing, yet they are clear and easy to read.

You can find the rules of dimensioning in a booklet published by the British Standards Institute (BSI). The booklet is number PD7 308. Your teacher will have a copy which you can look at. This booklet deals with engineering drawing. Another booklet, number BS 1192, deals with building drawing.

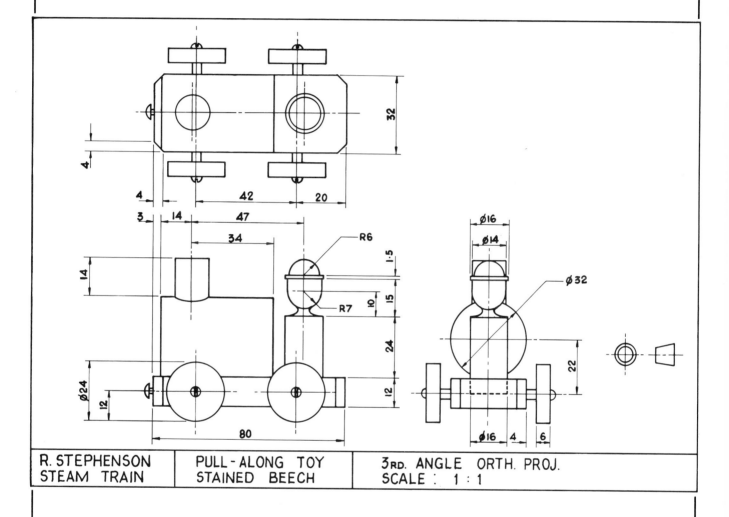

| R. STEPHENSON STEAM TRAIN | PULL-ALONG TOY STAINED BEECH | 3RD. ANGLE ORTH. PROJ. SCALE : 1 : 1 |

Key points

- Dimension lines should be lighter in weight than the outline of the object, so use a harder pencil.
- All dimensions necessary to define the object should appear on the drawing.
- A dimension should only appear once.
- Projection and dimension lines should be drawn as in the diagrams here.
- Arrowheads are clear, slender, solid and no more than 3 mm long.
- Dimensions should be in millimetres. They are read from the bottom and the left-hand side. (Look at the diagram.)
- Circles are dimensioned as shown in the diagrams here.

Information

The drawing of the toy has been completed by adding a **title block**. This contains all the information about the drawing. Remember to include the following: title of object, type of projection used, scale, material from which the object is to be made, name of person making the drawing, date and the drawing or reference number. Improve the appearance of your drawing by adding a border, as in the finished drawing of the toy train.

Activity 32 *You will design a building or a toy, from a number of prescribed units, and then make a dimensioned orthographic drawing of your design. The units, or modules, you can use are Liquorice Allsorts. Here are some simple drawings of the various sweets and their dimensions.*

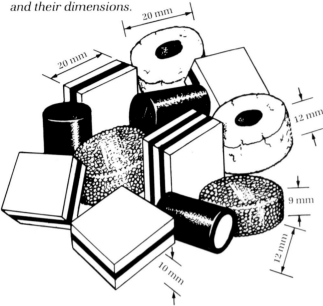

You can put the sweets together, as you wish, to make a simple toy or building. Look at the two examples, then use your imagination.

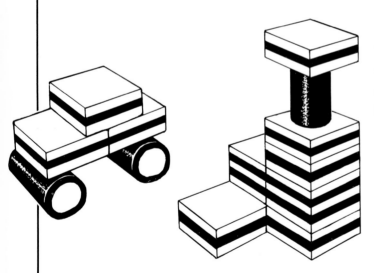

Decide on the design and then do a clear perspective sketch of the object. Proceed as follows, doing your working drawing on an A3 sheet of paper.

1 *Calculate the overall sizes – length, width and height.*
2 *Decide on the scale of your drawing.*
3 *Decide on the projection – first or third angle?*
4 *Work out the positions of the boxes into which the views will fit.*
5 *Complete the views.*
6 *Add dimensions, title block and border to complete the drawing.*

SECTIONAL VIEWS

You can show what is inside an object by drawing a **sectional view**. You draw what the object would look like if some of it were cut away, or a slice were taken through it. Think of some of the chocolate bars you eat. You find out what is inside, only when you take a bite. If you were designing a bar, you would need to do a cross-sectional view, like the one here. The ingredients could then be seen.

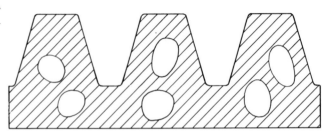

Activity 33 *Use squared paper. Make a freehand orthographic drawing of a chocolate bar, to your own design. Decide on the external shape and then on the ingredients. If you need to do some research before completing this activity, don't do it in the design studio!*

Formal sectional views

There are rules to follow for making a working drawing. Look at the example of a cross-section through a battery.

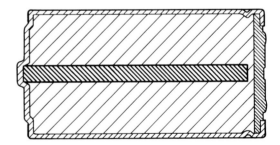

Key points

- Cross-hatch the cut surface – parallel lines at 45 degrees.
- Cross-hatch different parts in different ways.
- Show the plane of the section on an adjacent view.
- Label the section.

Activity 34 *Draw orthographic views of a biro or felt tip twice full size. (Refer to page 9 for details.) Make the front elevation a sectional view. Measure the pen you choose carefully, before you start to draw it.*

AXONOMETRIC PROJECTION

This drawing system tries to give a three-dimensional view of an object. It is constructed using a set square and a parallel motion. It does not try to allow for the effects of foreshortening. Axonometric projection is used particularly by architects. It is also known as a **plan oblique**. That name gives you a good clue as to where to start.

Start by drawing a true plan of an object, but inclined at an angle of 45 degrees. Project the vertical faces from the plan view. Add the top by using a 45 degree set square. If you wish to draw a cylinder or cone, the plan view will be a circle. It can be drawn with a compass.

Architects often produce a plan view of a building first, so this system is particularly useful for them. A quick visual of their building can soon be drawn. The plan does not have to be positioned at 45 degrees to the horizontal. You can tilt it either way, to emphasize one or other of the front faces.

Key points

- The plan is true and drawn at an angle to the horizontal.
- Project vertical lines from the plan.
- All measurements are true (or all are scaled by the same amount if necessary).

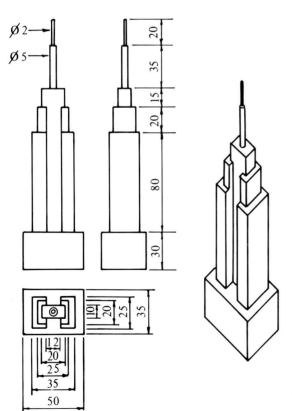

Activity 35 *Construct a view of the Empire State building from the simplified orthographic views given below. Start with the plan view and then project up the sides as required.*

The Empire State building has appeared in many films, notably King Kong and Superman. Add King Kong climbing up the building or Superman flying past it, to complete the drawing. Use the sketches on page 81. Make sure that you scale the drawings correctly.

Did you know... *The Empire State building was completed in 1931 and was the highest building in the world at 442 metres. Here are some of the remarkable statistics about the building: its volume is 37 million cubic feet and there are 2 million square feet of floor space; it contains 60 miles of water pipe, 3500 miles of telephone wire and it has 6500 windows, which are washed twice a month; there are 73 lifts in 7 miles of shafts; the fastest lift travels at 1200 feet a minute; on a clear day you can see about 80 miles from the top.*

Activity 36 *The tallest building in London is the National Westminster tower. The plan view of this building is the same as the NatWest logo given below. Make an axonometric drawing of the tower using this logo.*

logo   construction   plan of building

ONE-POINT PERSPECTIVE

You have already done a lot of perspective sketching. All types of perspective drawings can be constructed to a set of rules. One-point perspective is particularly useful for drawing interiors of rooms. It is used a lot by interior designers.

The main problem is deciding on the foreshortening which will take place. Follow this example. It shows how a room measuring 4 m wide by 6 m long and 2.5 m high is drawn in one-point perspective.

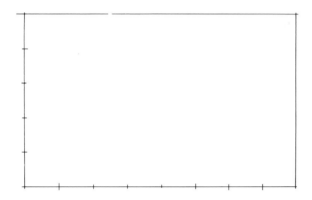

Decide which wall you will remove, so that you can see into the room. Draw the outline of the wall to a scale which will fit on your paper. Divide the edges of the wall into equal divisions. In this case each is equal to 0.5 m.

Draw in the horizon line. This will be at eye level. The average height of eye level is taken to be 1.5 m. Fix the vanishing point. If it is in the centre of the room, the drawing may look dull. Do not move it too far off centre unless you wish to show more detail on one side of the room.

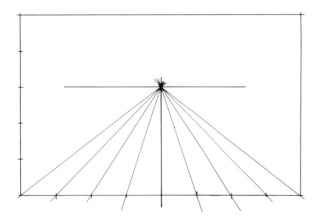

Project lines from the divisions to the vanishing point. Do this from the front edge only.

You can now find the effect of foreshortening by using a diagonal. Draw a diagonal from the horizon line to the furthest bottom front corner. The further point D is away from the edge of the room, the more distant is the viewing point. The closer it is to the frame, the nearer to the room is the viewing point. The drawing shows the method for finding a good viewing point.

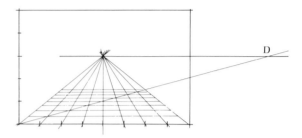

Draw horizontal lines where the diagonal crosses the radial lines. You have now divided the floor of the room into a grid that obeys the rules of perspective. Divide the sides and the ceiling in a similar way.

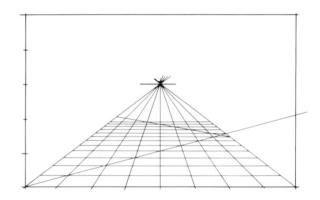

With your grid, you can now add the internal fittings and fixtures. Use the grid as an underlay. Do your final drawing on layout paper, or use a light box so that the grid can be clearly seen.

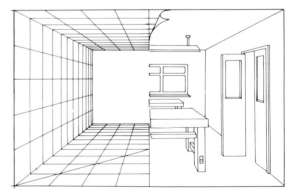

Activity *Choose a room at home and construct a one-point perspective of it. If the room has any features you dislike, redesign them. Include your ideas in your drawing. Show your completed drawing to your parents. Explain to them why you have made changes. Ask them for comments on your proposals.*

You can also use one-point perspective for objects. It gives a powerful impression of an object because of the foreshortening. You can reduce this by placing the vanishing point further away. Here are the stages in drawing an extending rule.

Draw the crate into which the object will fit. Begin with the true shape of the end, then select the position of the horizon line and the vanishing point which will lie on it.

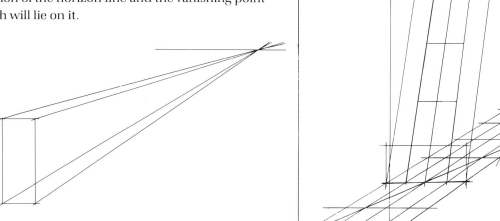

Divide the front edge into equal divisions and join these to the vanishing point. Use a diagonal to find distances towards the vanishing point.

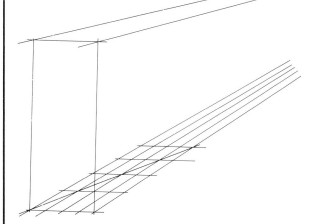

Draw a new diagonal to extend these divisions. You can find this diagonal from the final square drawn from the first diagonal. Subdivide the distance between the end and the vanishing point using this method.

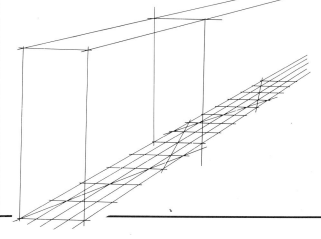

Project the grid on the base around the sides, to give the grid on which you will make the final drawing.

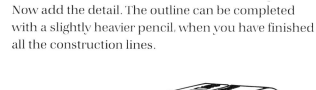

Now add the detail. The outline can be completed with a slightly heavier pencil, when you have finished all the construction lines.

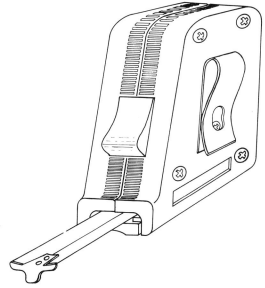

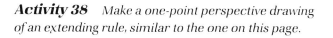

Activity 38 *Make a one-point perspective drawing of an extending rule, similar to the one on this page.*

Activity 39 *Choose a hand tool you use in the workshops and make a one-point perspective drawing of it. You might try a smoothing plane, hammer, electric soldering iron or a craft knife.*

ISOMETRIC PROJECTION

This drawing system is of the **paraline** type, like axonometric projection. That means that it is made up of parallel lines and does not allow for the effects of foreshortening. 'Iso' means equal, so isometric drawing is based on equal measurement.

To make an isometric drawing, you need a 60/30 degree set square and a parallel motion. You always start by drawing the box or crate into which the object will fit. To do this you need to know the overall height, width and length of the object.

Draw the front corner. In isometric projection, vertical lines remain vertical and horizontal lines are drawn at 30 degrees.

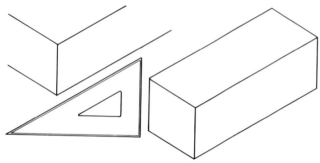

Once you have the front corner, measure the height, width and length along the correct lines. Draw in the front two faces.

The drawing is completed simply by adding the top using the 30 degree set square.

Isometric projection is used by engineers and others, for objects which are not too large. No shape in isometric is true - all the faces have been distorted. This system often makes something appear larger than it really is, but it is useful if you want a visual impression of an object reasonably quickly.

Key points

- Lines which are vertical on the object will be vertical in the drawing.
- Lines which are horizontal on the object will be at 30 degrees to the horizontal in the drawing.
- All measurements on paralines are true (or all are scaled by the same amount if necessary).

Isometric paper

Isometric paper helps your isometric sketching. The grid is in 5 mm sections, so you can do sketches without measuring, yet keep them in the right proportion. Look at this example.

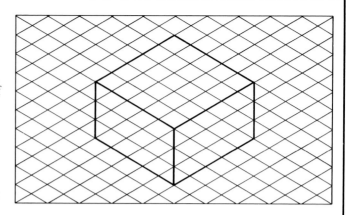

Isometric circles

There are no true shapes in isometric projection, so circles will also be distorted. They appear as ellipses. If you are sketching, just sketch the square into which the circle will fit. Find the four points where the square and the ellipse will touch, then sketch in the ellipse.

There is a more accurate method, when doing an isometric drawing with instruments. Suppose you need a drawing of a wheel. Draw the wheel and the square which contains it in orthographic projection. Add a grid to the wheel. Make the gap between the grid lines about 5 mm.

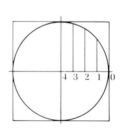
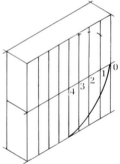

Draw the square in the correct position on the isometric drawing. Transfer the grid into the isometric view. Now transfer in turn, from the orthographic view to the isometric view, the distance from the centre line to where each grid line cuts the circle.

Complete the drawing by joining the points with a freehand curve. Find the back edge of the wheel by stepping off the thickness as shown.

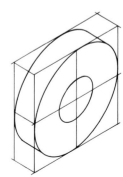

A measured isometric drawing

Look at the orthographic views of a packet and a tube of toothpaste. The drawings that follow show how to make an isometric view from these orthographic views. Start by drawing the packet. Work out the overall sizes. Draw a crate and then fill in the detail. Now draw the tube in the same way. Finish off by adding the top and the paste. Do not line in the drawing until you have completed all parts.

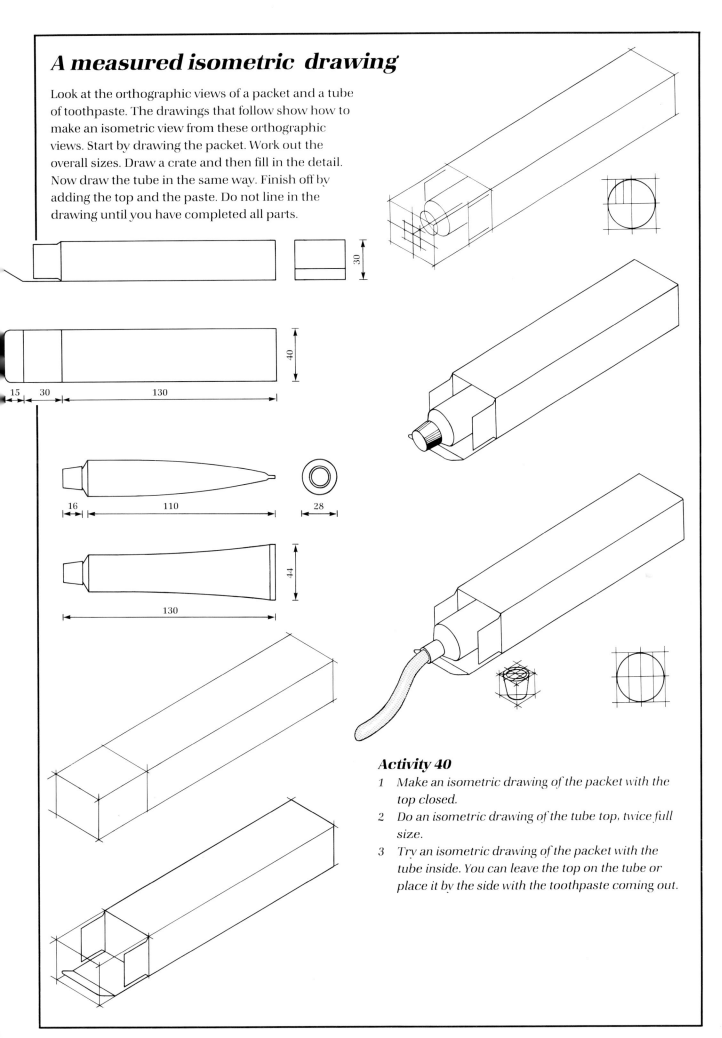

Activity 40

1 Make an isometric drawing of the packet with the top closed.
2 Do an isometric drawing of the tube top, twice full size.
3 Try an isometric drawing of the packet with the tube inside. You can leave the top on the tube or place it by the side with the toothpaste coming out.

EXPLODED VIEWS

Exploded views sound rather dramatic! This type of drawing can be used to show how parts of an object go together. They are used a lot in repair manuals and in booklets which explain how something works. When an object is exploded, you must draw the parts in relation to each other and in the same order in which they fit together.

Exploded views can be drawn in any drawing system. Pictorial views are normally used, but orthographic views can also be employed.

Here is an isometric view of a corner joint. It is difficult to see what the different parts will look like. An exploded view will help.

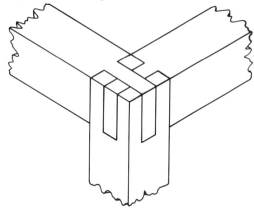

Draw the centre line through the joint. Draw the crates into which each part of the joint will fit.

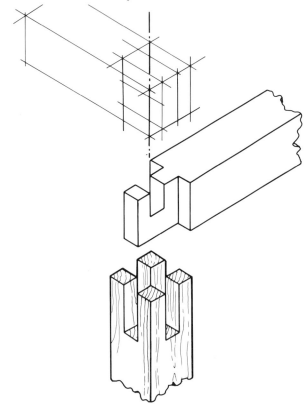

Draw each section, complete the outline and add texture to show the material of which it is made.

Here are the stages involved in making an exploded axonometric view of a co-axial TV aerial connector. Axonometric has been chosen, because the circles can be drawn with a compass.

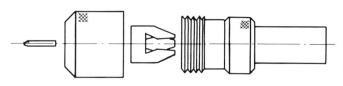

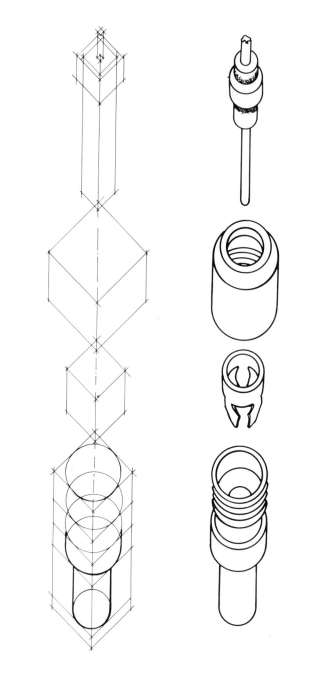

Activity 41 *Make an exploded drawing of one of the following: a three pin plug, a technical pen, a pencil sharpener, a plumbing compression joint, a can opener, or a lino print roller.*

48

Adding colour

COLOUR PENCILS

Colour pencils are one of the easiest and most versatile methods of colouring a drawing. They have many advantages.

- You can find colour pencils in a wide range of colours.
- Colour pencils are 'forgiving'. You can correct mistakes and errors quite easily with an eraser. Sometimes, however, some traces of the colour are left behind.
- You can mix colour to make the right value or **hue.**
- You can use the same pencil to give different tones, by varying the pressure.

Types of colour pencil

Colour pencils are usually made from a mixture of **chemical pigment** and **kaolin**, a type of clay. You can find two types of ordinary pencils: professional quality and children's colouring pencils. The professional pencil is harder, can be sharpened to a fine point and can, therefore, be used for drawing fine lines. Colouring pencils are softer, they are not available in such a wide range of colours and sometimes they are made in half length sizes. Coloured leads can also be bought for clutch pencils. These can be used for very fine detail work.

Water soluble pencils are also available in a wide colour range. This type of pencil is more difficult to use. You colour the drawing as normal and then use a watercolour brush. Use swift strokes to produce an even colour, removing the pencil marks.

Chinagraph pencils will write on all polished surfaces, such as china, glass and acetate sheet. Water and damp have no effect on the mark, yet you can remove it easily with a dry cloth. A limited range of colours is available.

Did you know... *You can change a colour in three ways. Many words are used to describe colour and these changes.*
Hue *This term describes the colour generally, e.g. red or orange, orange or yellow, a cornflower hue of blue.*
Intensity *This refers to the strength of the hue. Printers often use the word* ***saturation****. In television the word* ***chroma*** *is used.*
Tone *This term describes the amount of black present. Another word which is used is* ***value****. The opposite of tone is* ***tint****, which describes the amount of white present.*

Most designers specify a colour by giving a number from a book of samples. This is often called a colour ***swatch****. The most common colour system is the* ***Pantone Matching System****. The basic system has 505 numbered colours, plus high intensity and metallic colours.*

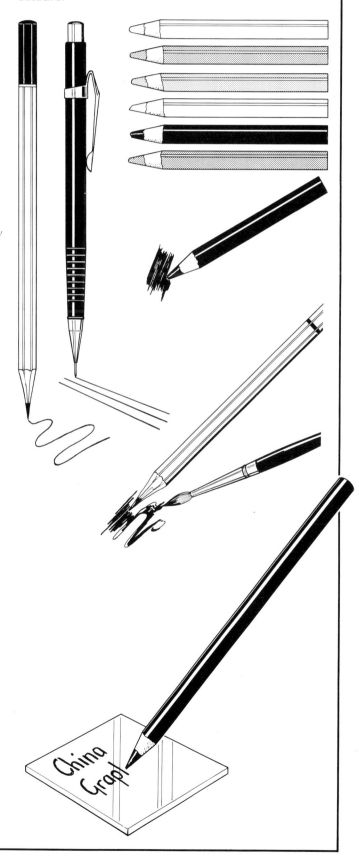

Experimenting with colour pencils

Colour pencils are used most commonly to add blocks of colour to a drawing. This helps to distinguish one part from another. It is important that you add the colour evenly. Practise shading differently shaped areas. Concentrate on creating an even surface. Avoid showing pencil marks. Use one colour pencil to produce four colour patches. Make the patches progressively darker in tone, as in the example shown below. You will find the lighter tones more difficult. Hold the pencil in the same way as you did when shading.

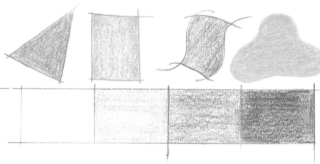

Smooth out the colour by **burnishing**. Do this by going over the colour with a white or light grey pencil. This process also lightens the intensity. Try burnishing parts of the colour patches you have already produced.

You can also use colour pencils to create a gradual change in tone. You will find this quite easy to do, by changing the pressure on your pencil. Draw some rectangles and shade them as shown, from a dark to a light tone.

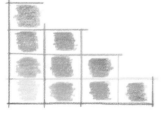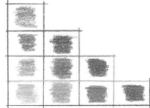

Even if you have only a few pencils, you can mix them to create a wide range of colours. Choose four coloured pencils and make a colour triangle like the one shown. The triangle is made up of ten separate patches of colour. Shade each in turn, starting with the darkest pencil being used. Add the other colours. You will see that four pencils give you a possibility of ten colours.

You can now start drawing some objects. Try some simple shapes, such as cubes, cylinders, cones and spheres. Use just one pencil for each shape.

Next use two pencils with a similar hue on each shape. The darker of the two can also be used to add a shadow.

Now put the shapes together. They will look like a pile of coloured building bricks. Remember to add the shadows which each brick will cast on the others. You can also colour the ground surface.

Using colour pencils

Diagrams   It is easier to understand an orthographic drawing if you use colour. It is easier to distinguish the different parts, as in the example below. Colour has been applied evenly to each area of this sectional view of a camera.

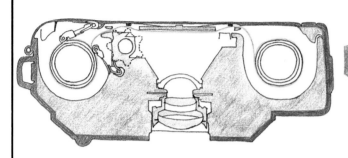

Plastics   You can render coloured plastics, such as acrylic, with colour pencils. Even a simple drawing, such as the design for a maze, can be improved by the addition of colour.

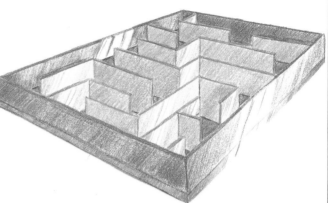

Background   You can use a colour pencil to make a line drawing stand out. Add a tone around the outline. The tone should be darker close to the object and decrease away from it.

Paint schemes   Colour pencils are useful when you are deciding on the colours with which you will paint an object. Use them for your possible schemes. Trial schemes for a simple book or cassette rack are shown below.

Wood   You can draw the different types of wood in common use with colour pencils. It is easier to show the detail and tonal variations of the grain with coloured pencils than with any other medium.

Activity 42   Make a sectional orthographic drawing of a stapler. Use colour pencils to distinguish between the various parts.

Activity 43   Design a simple maze similar to the one shown. The maze is 100 mm square with a 5 mm bearing ball. The maze will be constructed by laminating acrylic. Plan your maze using squared paper and then make a coloured axonometric drawing $1\frac{1}{2}$ times full size.

Activity 44   Produce some other examples of simple book or cassette racks. Sketch your ideas in one-point perspective and devise a painting scheme. Only use two colours.

MARKERS

The range of markers available can be quite bewildering. There are three basic differences.

1 The **ink** inside the markers varies. Some contain soluble ink and others contain permanent colourfast ink (usually oil or spirit based).
2 The **composition** of the nib varies. The most common nib materials are felt composition, fibre tipped, nylon, or foam. Felt nibs are easily damaged, but the others are more resilient to misuse.
3 The **size** and **shape** of the nib varies. Sizes range from fine nibs to broad nibs. They may be round, square, bullet, or chisel shaped.

You can find markers in a wide range of colours. When you have finished using these pens, always replace the caps. Do not use the spirit based pens in poorly ventilated areas.

Did you know...   *The human eye can see the difference between several million colours. Several thousand of these have been given names. The basic colour vocabulary in any language, however, is quite small. Variations in colour are described by adding another word, such as 'light' or 'dark', or by calling a colour after an object or material, for example orange, silver, or rose.*

*The first person to establish a test for colour consistency was a British brewer, Joseph Lovibond. He wanted to ensure that his beer had a consistent colour! The measurement of colour is known as **colorimetry**. Lovibond established a test with glass filters. His filters allowed 9 million possible arrangements. Computers can produce over 16 million different colours. It is a good thing that they do not all have names! How many names describing colour do you know? You have done very well if you can list 50.*

Special markers

Studio markers are available in a wide range of hues, tones and tints. They are usually of the permanent type. You can find some with two nib shapes, fine and broad. If you look after them well they last a long time. They can be reconditioned if they dry up, but they are expensive to buy.

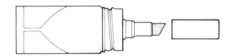

Brush markers have a nib like a paint brush. The soft foam tip is good for precision work, as well as for bold blocking in. These markers are available in a good range of water based colours.

White board markers are made mainly for working on white boards. They produce an even flat surface when used on paper.

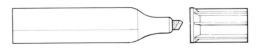

Materials used with markers

Bleedproof paper is advisable if you are using permanent markers. This paper stops ink from passing through onto the backing sheets. Never use ordinary layout paper when working on a drawing palette. Permanent markers will pass through the paper and permanently damage the surface of the board.

Tracing paper provides a good surface for marker drawings, as you can work on both sides of it. Tracing paper is non-absorbent, so markers will take longer to dry. Take care, otherwise you will smudge your drawing.

Often it is necessary to mask areas off, so that you get a sharp edge around your drawing. Use **masking tape** with scrap paper, such as old magazines. Check first that the tape can be removed without damaging the surface of the paper. If it does damage the surface, dust it lightly with talcum powder, to remove some of the stickiness. Alternatively, apply the tape to a polished surface, peel it off, then use it to mask around your drawing.

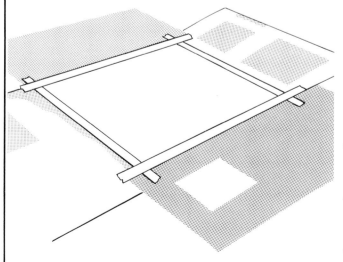

Masking film is a transparent film used to protect areas of a drawing where colour is not needed. Cover the entire drawing and then use a scalpel to cut out

the sections where you will add colour. Take great care when you are using a scalpel. They are extremely sharp. The film is known as **low tack.** This means you can remove it without damaging the paper's surface.

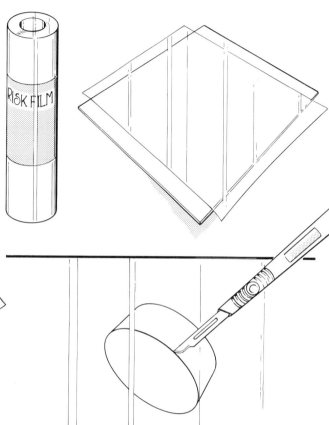

Key points

- Try a marker before using it on a design sheet. Find out all the line widths possible with the nib. Check the amount of **bleed** away from the nib. This is important when working to a line.

- Check that you are holding the pen correctly before applying it to the paper. Make a smooth quick stroke without allowing the nib to remain on the paper. If you do, colour will continue to flow from the nib.

- An area will become darker if you go over it twice with the same marker.

- Remember to clean the nib on a scrap of paper if you use one colour marker over another colour.

- Treat the nib with care. A damaged nib will produce poor results.

- Always replace the top after use to prevent the pen from drying out.

Practice with markers

Get used to holding and using the marker. Try to produce an even layer of colour, by making a series of parallel strokes. Try again using masking tape, so that you produce a square of even colour. Then, working in a rectangle, create a tone from dark to light by repeated use of the marker. Draw a series of lines and practise following the line. Markers do not allow a second chance, so practice is essential.

Once you have the feel of the markers, render the simple geometric shapes. It is difficult to create a shaded tone, so a different technique is used. Leave uncoloured bands of white paper to indicate reflected light. These should follow the form of the surface. On a sphere, the reflection often takes the form of a distorted window. You may need more than one marker for a cube. It is very difficult to make three different tones with the same marker. Find two markers with the same basic hue, but of different value. Render the third face of the cube with a double layer of the darker marker. Look at these examples and then try some yourself. Add shadow to the ground surface and any other adjacent solids.

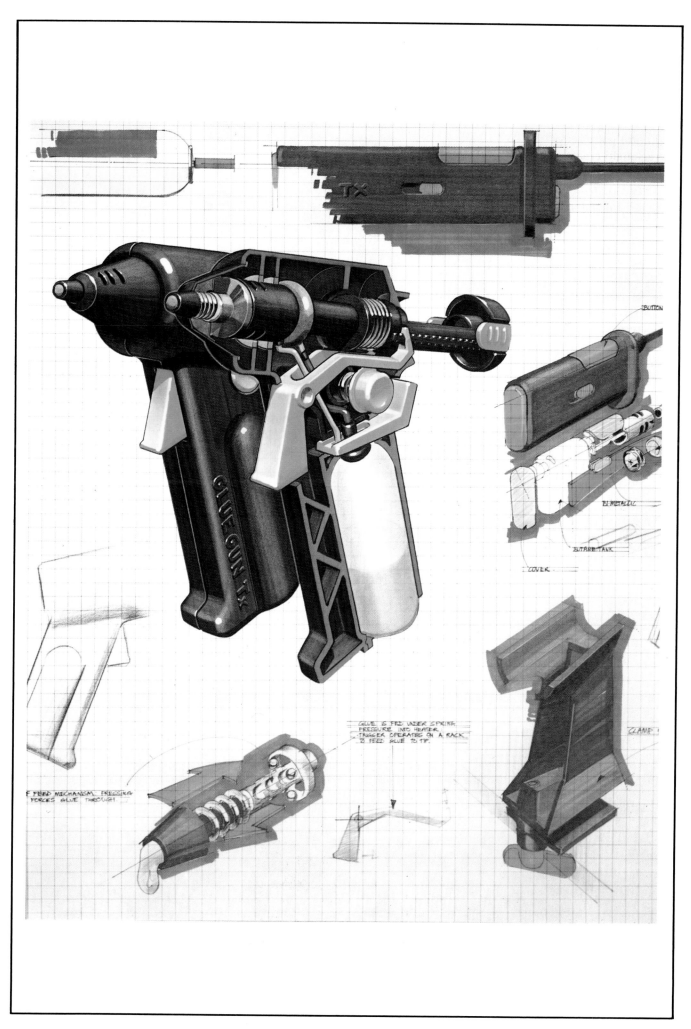

TX

GLUE GUN TX

BUTTON

BI METALLIC

BUTANE TANK

COVER

CLAMP

GLUE IS FED UNDER SPRING
PRESSURE INTO HEATER.
TRIGGER OPERATES ON A RACK
TO FEED GLUE TO TIP.

F FEED MECHANISM. PRESSING
FORCES GLUE THROUGH

Markers in use

The drawings on the previous page illustrate a new design for a portable glue gun heated by a self-contained butane heating element. Markers have been used to render the various drawings. Look carefully at the following:

- The range of drawing systems used - orthographic, one and two-point perspective, sectional and exploded.
- The method used to render simple shapes, such as cylinders.
- The use of the marker around the edge of the drawing, to make it stand out from the surface.
- **Highlights** - intense concentrations of reflected light also called **hot spots**, **bullets and farkles**. These are applied with a fine brush and **gouache**, or typewriter correcting fluid.
- The drawings have been rendered with the light coming from the left.
- The use of a dark marker to emphasize form.
- The rendering of the shadows cast by one part of the object on another part.

All of these points combine to produce a professional drawing. Remember that you must be able to draw the outline before you can render a drawing.

It is more difficult to render a drawing accurately with markers than with colour pencils. However, you can use colour pencils to sharpen up an edge or for a detailed part of a drawing. A white pencil is especially useful for adding low reflected light to a drawing rendered with markers.

Another way of obtaining a sharp edge is to cut the drawing out and then mount it on another sheet. Do this with great care, using a scalpel and a cutting mat. Use a thick piece of card, if you do not have a cutting mat. Never cut on a hard surface, such as a desk top or a drawing board.

*Activity 45   Return to Activity 26 and copy or redraw the telephone receiver. Follow the stages shown here to make a rendered drawing of the receiver. Start with a simple thumbnail sketch of the various tones which will appear on the receiver. Do this by actually looking at a telephone. This kind of drawing is called a **keyline** drawing. It should also show the light areas where reflections occur. Use this drawing to produce a rendered view of the receiver you designed - the one you cut out of card. Use the card as a template to produce a number of outlines on which to practise.*

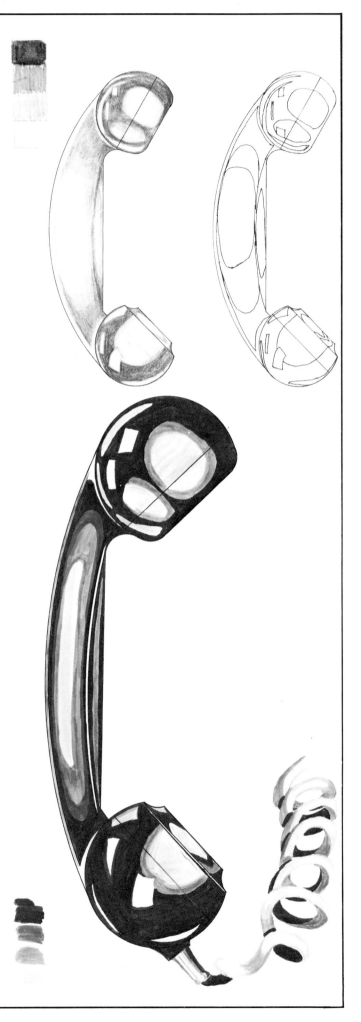

Activity 46   *A template is useful when several drawings are needed. For example, you might use a template when trying out the different effects of line, shape and colour on an object. Find an orthographic drawing of the side view of a car. (Look at advertisements, manuals and sales brochures.) Transfer the drawing onto thin card or plastic and make a template which you can draw around. Draw several outlines on an A3 sheet of paper with the template. Use markers to experiment with possible colour schemes. Try to make the car look thin and sleek, or short and stumpy. Use lines to emphasize speed and motion. Explore colour to give the car appeal to a young buyer or to make it appear respectable and sensible for an older driver. You are aiming to create a design sheet showing how the character and visual perception of a car can be manipulated.*

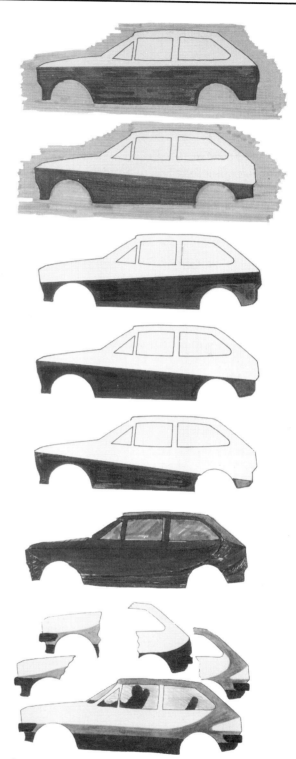

RENDERING A DRAWING

On the next two pages there are examples of the stages gone through in rendering a drawing. On the first page, coloured pencils have been used to produce a presentation view of the child's toy train. It has been drawn as if it were made from wood. On the second page, the train has been rendered with markers. This time it has been rendered as if it were made from plastic. The stages for each drawing are described below.

Colour pencil

1   The outline is drawn in pencil and transferred onto a clean sheet of paper.
2   Colour is applied to each area. Remember that the density of colour depends on the amount of light falling on each particular part.
3   A slightly darker colour is used to add the grain effect to each area.
4   The shadow is added where part of the toy is casting a shadow on another part.
5   The drawing is completed by adding the shadow that the toy is casting onto the surface on which it is resting.

Marker

1   The outline is drawn in pencil and transferred onto a clean sheet of bleedproof paper.
2   Colour is applied to each area following the key points already outlined.
3   The shadow is added where part of the toy is casting a shadow on another part.
4   The shadow cast by the toy onto the surface on which it is resting is added.
5   The drawing is completed by adding the highlights and cleaning up the outline with coloured pencils.

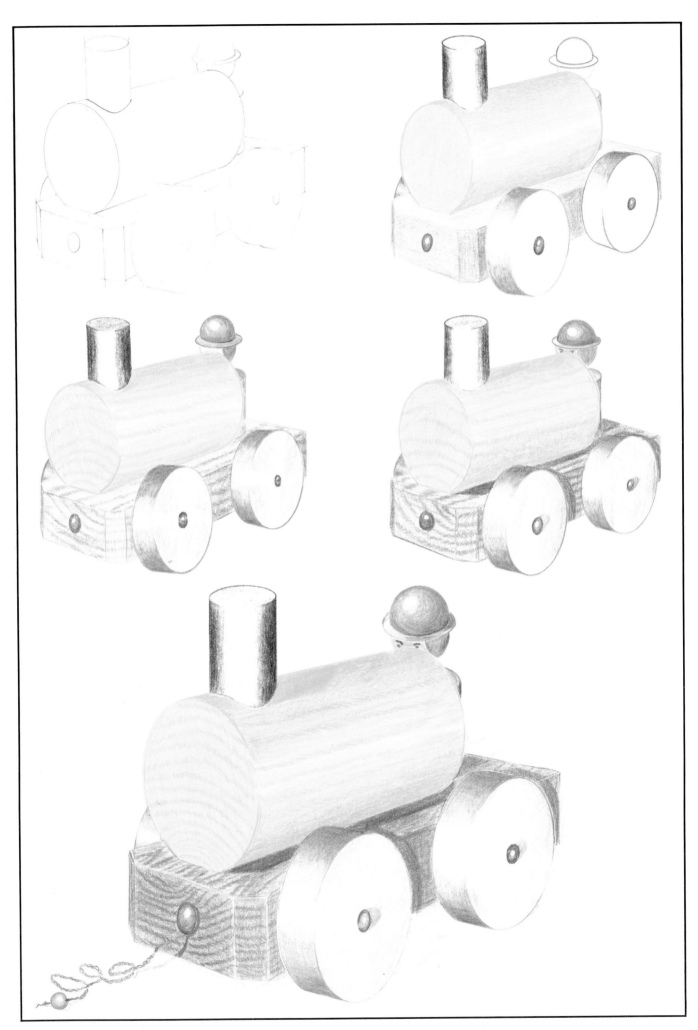

OTHER METHODS OF APPLYING COLOUR

Water colour

The most common type of paint used in rendering design drawings is **water colour**. The colour can be bought as a solid tablet or as a paste, and can be thinned with water. You can add very pale tints to orthographic drawings with great effect. You can also use water colour on presentation drawings.

Stretching paper

The paper should be **stretched**, unless you are using good quality paper. If the paper is not stretched, it will distort.

You need a flat firm board. Fill a sink with clean cold water. Pass the paper once through the water, hold it for a second or so over the water, to let the excess run off, then lay it flat on the board. Stick the paper down with brown tape - half on the paper, half on the board. It is important to stick the tape down firmly. When the paper has dried it will be perfectly flat. You can now make your drawing and colour wash it. It may cockle slightly, but it will dry flat. You can cut the artwork from the board, when completed and perfectly dry, using a scalpel and straight edge.

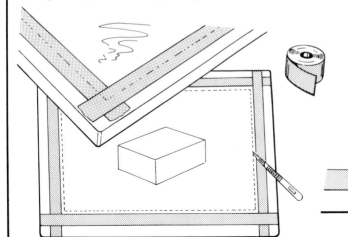

Applying a colour wash

Key points

- Set the board at a fairly steep angle.
- Mix sufficient wash to cover the area.
- Charge the brush with wash. Start at the top of the area and work across from left to right, and down. Pull the wash across the paper with the brush.
- Recharge the brush quickly and continue, if you run out of wash. Never stop while applying a wash to an individual patch.
- Complete the wash at the bottom of the area. Squeeze the brush out and use the dry brush to remove the surplus wash.
- Do not apply another wash to the area until the paper has dried.

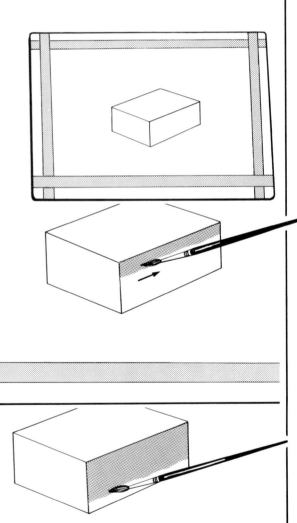

Wax resist

A wax crayon or candle can be used as a **resist** to water colour. Draw with an ordinary candle to make the paper waterproof beneath the wax. Add a wash and the waxed area will remain free of colour.

Wax crayons

These crayons are made from soft wax. They produce a solid bright colour on most papers and boards. It is very difficult, however, to produce different tones with wax crayons.

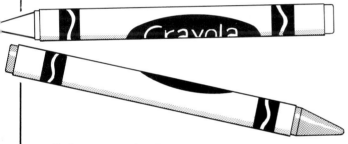

Chinese ink

Chinese ink is the stick form of Indian ink. You can dissolve it in water to produce a range of tonal greys. You can then render an object by applying a series of stripes. These stripes will follow the shading rules with which you are already familiar. A series of applications will change the stripes into a continuous tone. You can apply a colour wash over the Chinese ink, once completed and left to dry. It is a good idea to stretch the paper first.

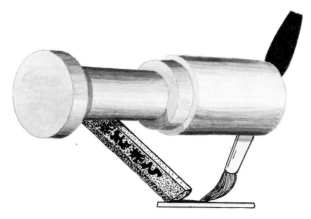

Spraying media

You should use masking whenever you spray colour onto a drawing. Either mask out the drawing if the background is being sprayed, or mask out the complete sheet and expose individual parts in turn.

You can use any aerosol spray containing colour. Always test the spray on a scrap of similar paper before using it on your drawing. You can use car re-touching sprays, but with great care as they quickly saturate a surface.

Using an old toothbrush is a cheap method. Dip the bristles in ink and then draw an old knife over the brush to make a variety of textures.

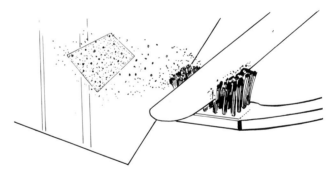

The most precise way of adding colour to a drawing is to use an **airbrush**. You need a lot of skill to use it successfully. You can buy a simple form of airbrush which uses a marker as the source of colour. It produces effective results and is simple to use.

Activity 47   *Design a simple skittle and produce a three-dimensional drawing of it. Use markers or a spray technique to produce a rendered drawing of the skittle. Some examples are shown on the next page.*

Activity 48   *Make a pictorial drawing of a hand-held object, such as a hairdryer, a clock, a camera, or a calculator. When you have done the outline, render it with the medium you find the easiest to use. On the next page there are two examples - a telephone for which coloured pencils were used and a steam iron rendered using water colour. These were done by professionals. You can learn a lot by looking at their drawings.*

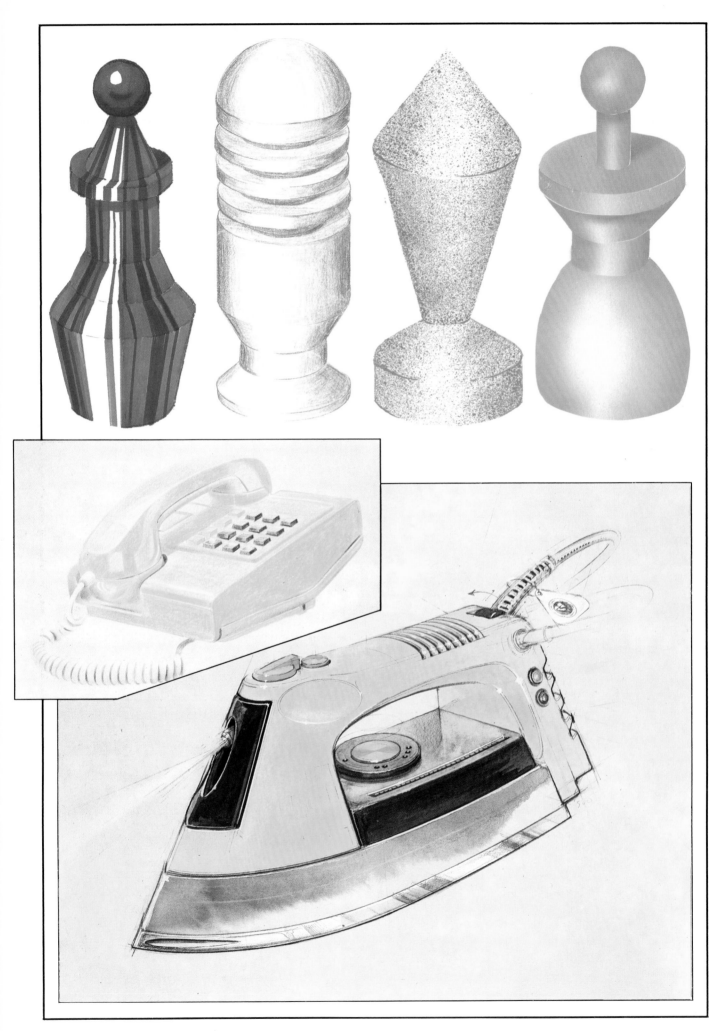

DRAWING FROM NATURE

The natural world is a rich source of ideas. Observe nature carefully and you may find the inspiration to solve a problem. Your observation will be sharper and more accurate if you record what you see by drawing. Nature may help you when you are faced with aesthetic or functional problems.

The drawings below are from a design sheet based on flowers - toadflax, a wild flower, and fuchsia, a cultivated flower. Careful drawings have been made of the flowers. This requires an understanding of the form. A mask has been used to concentrate attention on one area. A magnifying glass can be used to observe even greater detail. The flowers have been taken apart and some elements have been drawn on a larger scale. From the wild flower, an idea has been developed for a cast pewter pendant. It will be completed by infilling the sunken areas with cold cure resins. A pattern for a tile for the top of a coffee table has been evolved from studying the fuchsia.

Activity 49   *Make a careful study of a natural object - a shell, a seed, a flower, a stone, a piece of bark - anything which you find visually interesting. Use your study to produce a design for an item of jewellery or for a tile for the top of a coffee table.*

Layout and presentation

The reason for drawing is often to communicate an idea to other people. You are now familiar with several drawing systems. These allow ideas to be exchanged and understood. It is also important that information should be clearly and attractively presented. Give some thought to the way that you will record your ideas, before you start work on a design brief. Remember to record your thoughts whenever you think about the problem.

Always keep a **project notebook**. This is a personal record of the project. It will include all of your ideas, research carried out, target dates to which to work, checklists of things to do and any other details which will be important in reaching a solution.

You may also compile a **project folder** or **design report**. When you start design work, this may be only one or two sheets. As projects become more complex, so will the reports. If you are a professional designer, you should take as much care with the report as with the end product.

TIPS ON PAGE LAYOUT

You must first decide on the size of your report. The smallest size you will use is probably A4, and the largest is probably A2. Perhaps the most convenient size is A3. The size of report may depend on the nature of the brief.

The border

A freehand line around the edge of the paper will help to improve the appearance of even the most basic sketches. This can be done using the edge of the paper as a guide. Use the other hand to steady the paper.

A quadrant instead of a square corner provides a more interesting frame. It also gives the drawings greater authority, as it resembles a television screen. You can adapt the border to provide space for the heading or page number. There are many other border variations which you can use. Try designing your own.

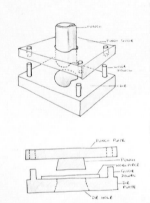

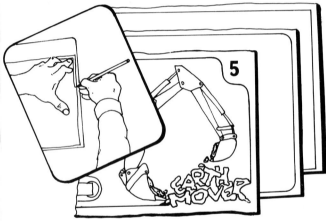

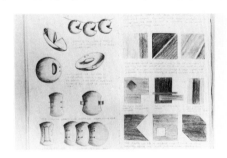

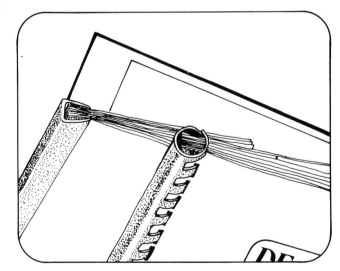

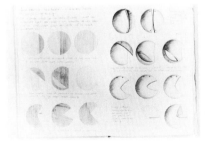

If the sheets are to be bound, make the border on the left-hand side wider than on the right-hand side. This will allow room for the binding and ensure that none of the drawing is hidden.

Working area

The **working area** is the space inside the border. It should be similar for each page. Pages should be laid out so that they are easy to read. (We talk about reading a drawing as well as reading text.) Work on a page in a logical fashion. We are all conditioned in this country to read pages from top to bottom and from left to right. Sketch ideas in this order and it will be easy for others to follow the way your thoughts developed.

Pages will often include notes as well as drawings. These will be easier to read if they are on the opposite side of the sheet to the binding. Notes can be placed in a separate border - some suggested layouts are shown below.

COMPILING A DESIGN REPORT

A design report should be arranged in a logical progression, probably in the order in which you tackled the design brief. Number each page and use headings for each page or section as appropriate. An index might be useful if there are a number of pages. A cover is also a good idea, because it will protect your drawings. You can use it to illustrate the project. Perhaps you can design a pictorial word for the cover. It could also be used inside the report. Remember that once it is drawn, you can trace it using a light box. The sections in your report will be similar to the stages in solving the design problem.

Use of a grid

Designers often use a **grid** to ensure that pages in a report or book, or panels in an exhibition, have a similar appearance without being identical. If each page or panel were identical, the report or exhibition would appear tedious or dull. The design of this book is based on a grid consisting of two or three columns. A possible grid for A3 paper is shown below with some examples of page layouts using the grid.

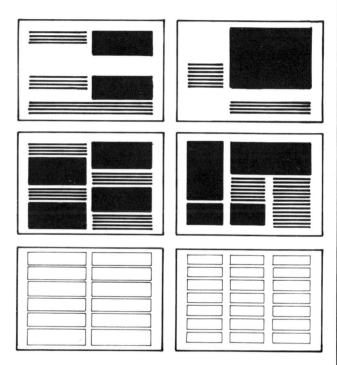

MOUNTING DRAWINGS

Often it is necessary to remount drawings so that they can be included in your report. First you must work out the exact size of the drawing and draw a frame around it accurately. You can then cut out the drawing using a modelling knife, scalpel, or guillotine. Scissors rarely produce straight edges. Next mark carefully the position of the drawing on the finished page. Use a base line or dots in the corner. Do this very lightly, with a pencil so that it will not show. Finally, apply adhesive to the back of the drawing, position it accurately and carefully smooth it down. Always place a clean piece of paper on top of the drawing before smoothing it down with your hand.

Adhesives

Spray mount comes in an aerosol. It is clear and allows drawings to be repositioned. You only need to spray one surface and you can use it on the thinnest tissue. Take great care when using spray mount. Only use it in a well ventilated room. Place the work being sprayed on some scrap paper, direct the nozzle and then carefully spray the required surface. Do not overspray.

Rubber cement comes in tins or tubes. Apply it evenly with a spatula to the back of your drawing. It allows for repositioning and you can easily remove excess cement by rubbing it gently into a ball.

Stick adhesives are easy to apply. The adhesive is a white plastic PVA (polyvinylacetate). Rub the stick carefully over the back of the drawing, position it carefully and then smooth it down.

Window mounting

Window mounting can improve the appearance of a presentation drawing. Cut a hole in a sheet of paper and mount the drawing from the back. Hold it temporarily in position with masking tape. Turn it over to check it is in the right place. Mount it permanently with gum strip when you are happy with the position. Do not use Sellotape, as it can shrink and cause distortion. Window mounts can be any shape - they do not have to be rectangular.

BINDING A REPORT

There are several ways of assembling a report. A **hole punch** can be used and then a lace threaded through. The paper often tears around the hole, so use reinforcements or thin plastic supports on the front and back. Simple **plastic slides** on spines come in a number of forms. These are cheap and efficient. If you use a cover, make sure it is flexible enough to allow the report to be opened easily.

SPECIAL LAYOUTS

Sometimes a design idea or drawing is so complex that you will need special techniques to communicate the information effectively. Exploded and sectional views are two methods which have already been explained. Two more are shown here.

Balloon drawings

When the relationship of detailed information to a broader background needs to be shown, a **balloon drawing** is a good solution. Show the links in the background and superimpose the detail on a larger scale in balloons or windows. The example shows this being used on a location map. Other uses are production lines where a sequence of stages needs to be shown.

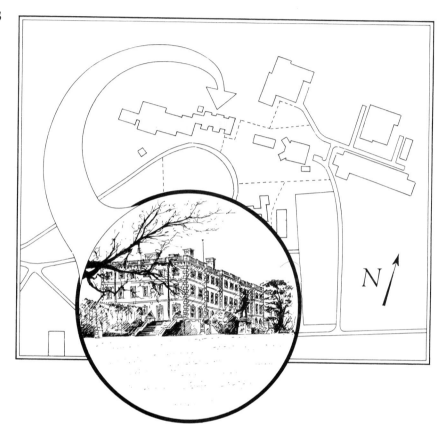

Overlay

When a drawing is very complex, you can sometimes break it down into various stages. Draw each stage on a sheet of clear acetate that flips over the basic drawing. You can use this technique in many ways - to show possible colour combinations on a line drawing, to show different solutions to a layout problem, the base drawing being a ground plan, or to show the various components on a mechanical drawing. This technique is often used on an overhead projector to build up information.

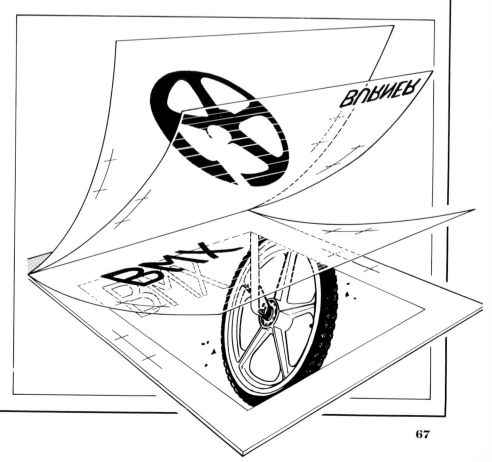

Making models

WHY USE MODELS?

Materials such as wood, metal and plastic are expensive. Before starting to realize a solution in the most suitable material, it is a good idea to make a **model**. A model is a three-dimensional (3-D) representation of a possible design. A model is often smaller than the real thing (scaled down), or it may be the actual size. Very rarely is a model larger than the final product. Models can be divided into three types: **exploratory**, **prototype** and **demonstration** models. The term model is also used in computer graphics.

Key points

Before you start to make a model, consider the following points:

* Decide on the exact purpose of the model.
* Decide on the level of detail which will be needed.
* Use the most appropriate materials to make the model (often the cheapest).
* Choose a suitable scale for the model.
* Think carefully about the method of construction.

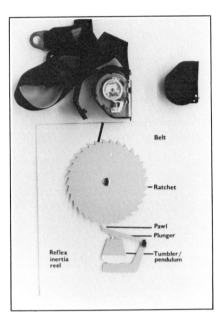

TYPES OF MODELS

Exploratory models are used to investigate an idea. You can make them from cheap or scrap materials, such as those shown on the next page. They are used to visualize an idea and to help reach a solution. You may make several before you find the best solution. You might use them to check sizes and proportions, or to discover if an idea will perform as required.

Prototype models serve a different purpose. If a product is to be made in any quantity, the manufacturing and production costs will be considerable. A prototype is made before making this commitment. This is a model which resembles exactly the final object. It is made to confirm that the best solution has been achieved. A prototype is made with a great deal of care and accuracy. A range of techniques and tricks are used, so that visually it is difficult to distinguish the prototype from the real thing. Some prototypes actually work, others are just visually identical.

Demonstration models are used to explain an idea or a principle, to prove that the final product will work. They may be simplified or scaled down - they may even be two-dimensional (2-D). The key factor is that they operate in a similar way to the final product. You may use demonstration models to describe how a system operates, whether it be mechanical, hydraulic, or pneumatic. Other systems, such as the flow of cars in a car park or the possible arrangement of a modular furniture system, might also require modelling. Demonstration models are also useful as teaching aids.

EQUIPMENT

Very few tools are needed. You will need something with which to cut the materials, such as a craft knife or a scalpel. You must also have a surface to cut on and a straight edge to cut against. You can buy special self-sealing cutting mats, but a thick sheet of cardboard or blockboard will do. You will also need a range of glues, depending on the materials you are using. Contact adhesives are suitable for card, but take care if you use them on plastic. Most plastics require a special cement. Polystyrene, PVC and expanded polystyrene all require different adhesives. The wrong adhesive will either fail, or damage the materials being joined. It is often difficult to know exactly the type of plastic when using scrap materials, so check the adhesive on a small piece first. Files and wet-and-dry paper are also useful for removing unwanted material and for tidying up joints when working with plastics.

MATERIALS

Exploratory models

Use any suitable material for exploratory model making. The possible uses of scrap materials, such as those illustrated, are endless. The only limit to their use is your imagination. Unwanted packaging material is particularly useful. Cardboard packets can be taken apart and quickly turned into the shapes and forms you need. Plastic cartons are also useful. Drinking straws are good for modelling structures, as are cocktail sticks and toothpicks. Cardboard tubes can be used for cylinders, and wooden beads and table tennis balls are useful for spherical shapes.

You can use balsa wood and jelutong (a similar low density wood) to create forms which cannot be produced from scrap materials. You can use softer materials, such as clay and Plasticine, where complex shapes are required. Take care though, as objects made in malleable materials are often difficult to realize in harder materials. Use paint to unify a model which has been made from a range of materials.

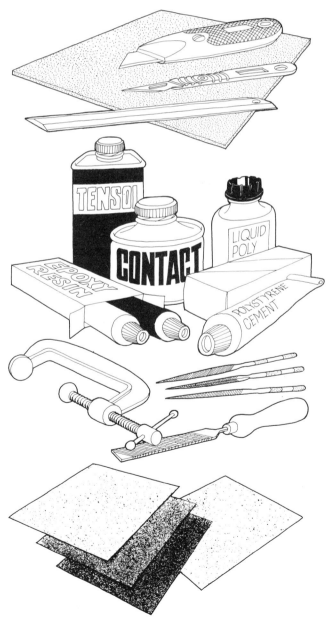

Prototype models

Prototype models often need special materials. Plastic sheet, either polystyrene or Perspex, is generally used. Specific cements should be used for joining these materials. Tensol No. 12 is used for joining Perspex, and liquid poly or Mek-pak for joining polystyrene sheet. You can create textured surfaces using scrap plastics, textured card or abrasive paper. Any suitable material can be used - you will integrate it into the model when you paint it. A **filler**, such as plastic padding or Isopon, is used to fill joints and smooth corners. Use **transfer lettering** or **moulded plastic lettering** to add instructions and names. The best method of applying paint is to use a spray. This is easiest with an aerosol, such as those used to retouch car paint work. Only use a spray in a well ventilated room and preferably with the correct extraction equipment. Drawing tapes and the 'go faster' stripes used on cars can be added to complete a prototype.

Demonstration models

Card is probably the most useful material, although plastic sheet can be used. Many bits and pieces are used to make flexible units in a mechanical model. Use paper fasteners and a hole punch, an eyelet machine and brass eyelets, or press studs which can be bought in a dressmaker's shop. You can demonstrate mechanical systems using Fischer Technic or Lego kits. Such kits allow ideas to be modelled quickly. Elastic bands are useful in card models, to indicate springs and to keep a model in tension. Clear acetate or film is also useful, so that you can add information on an overlay.

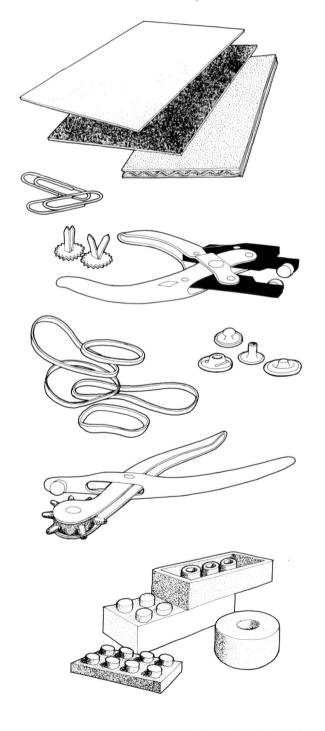

DEVELOPMENTS

A **development** is a flat shape which can be bent or folded to produce a three-dimensional form. A rectangle is the simplest development - bend it around and it becomes a cylinder. The drawing below is the development of a paper aeroplane. Fold it in the right places and the flat sheet becomes a solid form which will fly.

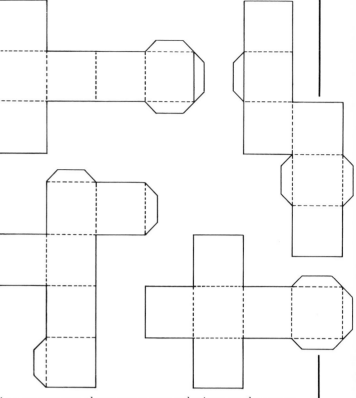

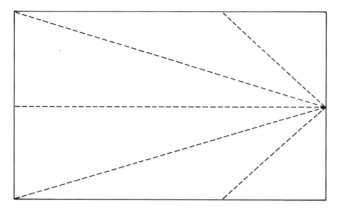

Developments are used when working in sheet material, such as card, plastic, fabric, leather, or metal. For example, you could use developments to construct a model where a solid form is required. Boxes, cylinders and cones are quick to make. Simple forms can be put together to make more complicated ones. Below are the constructions for drawing the developments of these simple forms. Flaps are necessary so that you can glue the developments together.

As you can see, there are many solutions to the same problem. Look at the cardboard boxes used to package the things which we buy. All of them are made from developments. Many of the clothes we wear have also been made from developments, which are called **patterns.** Here is an example. For what item of clothing is it a pattern?

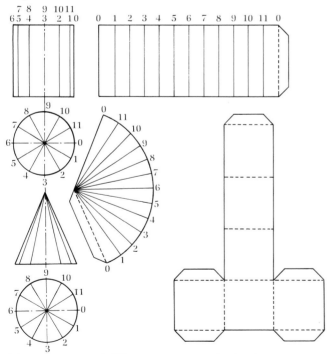

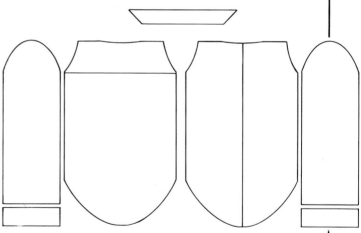

There are several different ways in which a box can be formed from a development. Look at the examples. Each development, folded up, will form an identical box.

Activity 50 *Find a cardboard box which is no longer needed. Take it apart carefully and work out the development from which it was made. Draw out the development accurately on a piece of A4 paper. Give it to a friend and see if he or she can construct the box.*

Activity 51 *Use paper developments to make a model of the simple space craft you designed in Activity 7. Remember to colour your developments before you fold and glue them.*

MODEL-MAKING EXAMPLES

Exploratory models

Brief Design and make a seed propagator which can be sold as a flat pack. It should be possible to disassemble the propagator when it is not in use, so that it can be easily stored.

This design brief required careful thought before ideas could start to be modelled. Two important questions had to be answered at the beginning. What size and shape should the propagator be? From which material should it be made? Careful research produced answers to the questions. Seed trays are produced in standard sizes, so it makes good sense for the propagator to be designed around this size. A decision was taken that the propagator should hold three trays and that they would be arranged in a row.

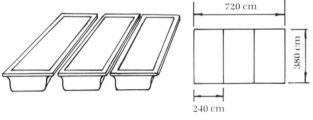

Safety had to be considered in choosing the material. The chosen material would have to be folded repeatedly without breaking and be stored without damage. Above all, it had to be available in a transparent or translucent form so that sunlight could shine through it. The material chosen was corrugated polypropylene. Polypropylene withstands continual bending (as when used for integral hinges on plastic boxes). In its corrugated form, it is light, strong and relatively cheap. It is only available in translucent form (about 76% optical efficiency), but that is satisfactory.

The main problem was how to turn a flat sheet into a strong solid box with a detachable, but relatively airtight, lid. From sketches of overall appearance, possible developments were drawn and paper models were produced. Gradually the best idea emerged.

More accurate scale models of the solution were made in a similar, but scrap, material - corrugated cardboard, easily reclaimed from cardboard boxes.

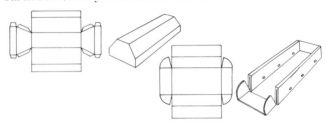

The final development was drawn out accurately, now all the problems were solved. It was then transferred to the corrugated materials and cut out with great care. The base was made of opaque polypropylene which did not need to be translucent. The material was joined by using interlocking mechanical joints and press studs. In the final product, a heating cable was added to help maintain a constant temperature of about 12-15°C. This was buried in sand in the base. The brief was successfully solved. In this example, the making of simple models was more appropriate, in reaching a solution, than drawing.

Activity 52 *Design and make in cardboard a scale model of a portable container for one of the following: records, tape or video cassettes, fishing tackle, needlework and dressmaking equipment, a school packed lunch, picnic things, graphic equipment, or a collection of semi-precious articles such as fossils or coins.*

The container should be made from one or more developments and should be capable of being unfolded and stored flat. The final product, if made, will be constructed from corrugated polypropylene. Develop your ideas using simple paper models.

Prototype models

Brief Design and make a prototype model of a simple device that can be used to pick up small steel objects, such as pins and needles. The body of the final product will be injection moulded in two parts.

The purpose of this page is to show you how to set about making such a model. The story starts at the point when the design has been completed, a working drawing has been made and model making is about to begin.

The model is to be made from styrene sheet. This material can be easily shaped. A craft knife is used to mark the material, which can then be snapped by pressing along the scored mark. It can also be cut using a piercing saw, but that is time-consuming. If the sheet material needs to be shaped, this can be done with heat. Place the material in a cool oven, about 120°C. When it has become soft, bend it to the required shape. It is best to have a simple wooden former, to ensure that the shape is accurate. Secure the plastic to the former and then cool it in cold water.

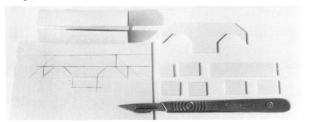

When all the individual pieces of the body have been shaped, they can be assembled. First make sure that the edges of the side pieces are square. Place a sheet of wet-and-dry paper on a flat surface and then rub the styrene sheet on it. This is the simplest method.

The joint is then made as shown below. The solvent is brushed along the joint with a small paint brush - it is drawn into and along the joint by **capilliary action**. When the solvent has evaporated, the joint is secure. The main body can be assembled and strengthening ribs added if needed.

If the exterior shape is not quite right, it can be built up with extra styrene sheet. Filler can be used to smooth in irregularities. When hardened, excess may be removed with wet-and-dry paper.

The prototype must look exactly like the finished article, so extra detail now needs to be added. The production model is to be made in two parts, so a break line must be added. This is scored onto the surface using a shaped tool. The name of the product will be moulded into the finished article. This effect can be achieved by adding moulded plastic letters.

When the body is finished, it is sprayed. This is best done by hanging the object from a cotton thread in an area with appropriate extraction. A series of fine layers are applied, gradually building up to the required colour. Fine wet-and-dry paper is used to remove the spray from the lettering so that it stands out. The prototype is completed by adding the mechanism and the control knob. The final article is visually identical to the production model and it also works.

Activity 53 *The steel objects are attracted to the pin picker by a magnet. The magnet is moved vertically up and down inside the body of the device by the control knob - when down, the objects are picked up, and when up, the objects are dropped. How is this movement achieved? Sketch as many possible solutions as you can think of.*

Activity 54 *Design one of the articles listed below and then make a prototype model using the procedures described in the example above. All of the items would be made by injection moulding if manufactured.*

1   *A bathroom tidy (toothpaste/brush/beaker).*
2   *A gauge for measuring the amount of spaghetti to be cooked per person.*
3   *A scraper for removing ice from a car windscreen.*

Demonstration models

Brief Design and make a model which will demonstrate how something works.

Demonstration models can be used either to explain the operating principles of a man-made object, or to see if an idea has the potential to work. This example is a model to explain the workings of an inertia reel seat belt.

First a careful examination of a seat belt mechanism is made. Observations are recorded in a series of sketches from which the model can be made.

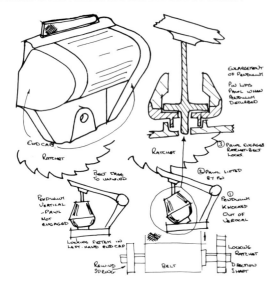

From these sketches, the operation is simplified so that the model will be relatively easy to understand. The various components are drawn separately. A simple paper model using pins and card as a base is then made, to check if the model will work.

A scale is chosen for the model. In this case the model is being scaled up ten times, as some of the components are rather small.

All the separate elements of the model are cut out of card. They are assembled loosely so that the layout can be checked.

Each part is now coloured using the most appropriate method – coloured paper, felt markers, or pens. Once rendered, they are assembled. In this case, press studs are being used. Press studs allow parts to rotate and also allow the model to be taken apart (which is very useful if the model is being used as a teaching aid). Dismountable mechanical models are easy to make using press studs.

The completed model is mounted on a backboard with annotation to explain exactly what happens. Can you work out why this seat belt locks instantly when a sudden movement is transmitted via the belt to the mechanism?

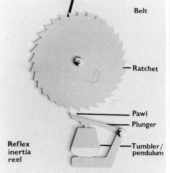
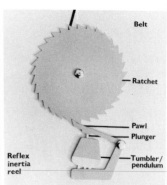

Activity 55 *Make a demonstration model to explain the mode of operation of a man-made device. Here are some possible suggestions: pumps, cranes, earthmovers, engines, locks, sewing machines and typewriters.*

Computer graphics

Computers affect every aspect of your life, including the ways in which drawings and visual images are produced. Computers are powerful tools which can perform complex tasks extremely quickly. You may be familiar with how to use a microcomputer. Although microcomputers have very limited power compared with the computers used in industry, they can be used to carry out similar operations.

At present, the graphic tasks you can give a school computer are restricted. This will change rapidly. Equipment is becoming available which will let you explore the potential of computer graphics. Soon you will be able to use the computer to aid your design work and help you solve practical problems.

THE COMPUTER GRAPHICS WORK STATION

You need to become familiar with several pieces of equipment before you can use a computer to produce graphics. Let us look at what is needed. This explanation will also make you familiar with some of the words and terms used in computing.

There are two main categories: **hardware**, the equipment you can see and touch, and **software**, the instructions given to the computer. The software is the information or **program** on which the computer works.

The central processor   This is the computer, a machine which handles information according to instructions or programs. You will begin by using a **microcomputer** or **micro**. A micro consists of a **microprocessor** which controls operations and the **memory** which holds data and programs. Built into the cabinet is the **keyboard**, the most common method of communicating with the computer. The micro controls all the other hardware linked into the system.

The power of a computer is measured in **kilobytes** (K). A **byte** is a group of eight **bits**. (A bit is a single binary digit, the ultimate unit of computer information.) A byte is the basic unit and defines a **character**. A typical micro will have a memory capacity of 64 K bytes (512 000 bits). This memory is in two forms. **ROM** – read only memory – is unalterable. It contains the programs which control the micro's operating language. **RAM** – random access memory – is the memory available to the user. It can store and operate additional programs. RAM is not permanent – it is lost when you turn off the computer.

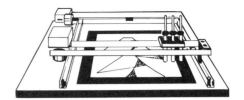

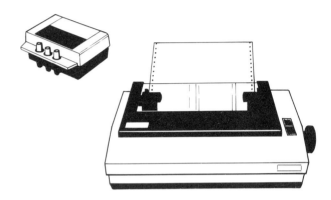

The display screen   This is how the computer communicates with you. It is known as the **VDU** or **visual display unit**.

The data storage unit   This device or **peripheral** enables information to be fed into the micro. The simplest method of storing information is on a **tape cassette**. You can load this into the computer using a cassette player. For more complex and rapid information handling, you can use a **floppy disc** and a **disc drive**.

The output device   The completed graphic image can be stored on disc or tape. However, you might need **hardcopy**, a drawing on a piece of paper. You can obtain this via a **printer** (dot matrix variety for graphics) or a **flatbed pen plotter**.

HOW IS A PICTURE DRAWN?

The screen is made up of many small cells. These are known as **pixels**. Each pixel can either be lit in a range of colours, or unlit. The number of colours depends on the computer that you are using and on the program you are running. The pixels can be built up to produce lines, curves and shapes, which in turn can be used to create objects which have form. The more pixels there are across and down the screen, the finer will be the detail. This is called the **resolution**. The higher the resolution, the finer will be the image. The quality of the image is controlled by the amount of RAM available and the quality of the VDU. (High resolution VDUs are available for graphics.)

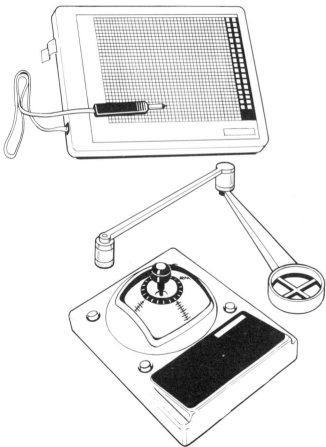

The input device   This is the part through which the information is fed into the system. On a micro this is often the keyboard, but there are a number of other input devices, such as a **light pen**, a **digitizer**, a **joystick**, a **touchscreen**, or a **tracer arm**. Still frame cameras and video cameras can be used with more powerful computers.

STARTING COMPUTER GRAPHICS

Most micros are sold with a user manual or guide, and some demonstration software. The software will give you an idea of what your micro can do. There are probably some examples of the micro's graphic capability included in the software. It will take a lot of time and patience to master the procedures required to produce images like those on the demonstration software.

The manual will explain the stages in loading and running a program. This is quite straightforward. Once you have mastered this, you can use any of the commercial software. Software is relatively expensive, so buy wisely. Check out exactly what a program can and cannot do. There are a number of specialist magazines that review all new software, so see what they think before buying. On page 79 there is an outline of the types of graphics programs currently available. Remember that you must buy a program which has been written specially for your machine, as each machine has a different language.

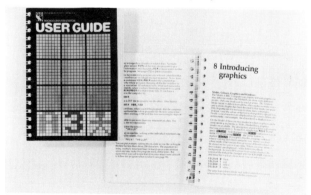

You will probably want to try producing some graphics yourself. Your micro's manual will show you how to start. Your manual is invaluable, but the following may help you to understand the two ways of producing images.

An image on the screen can be produced either by using the **graphics commands** and treating the screen as a grid of individual points, or by using the **text commands** and treating the screen as a grid of blocks in which characters can be placed.

Graphics commands treat the screen as a grid. This means that any point can be defined by x and y co-ordinates. You can think of the screen as graph paper, with the origin (0,0) usually in the bottom left-hand corner. On the BBC model B microcomputer, for example, there are 1280 points horizontally and 1024 points vertically (1310 720 points in total). No micro is powerful enough to make that number of points available to the user. Each pixel seen on the screen is made up of a small block of these points. A command affecting any one point will actually affect the whole pixel which contains that point.

How many pixels will be available? That depends on your computer. Most micros have different **operating modes**. Each mode will use the RAM in a different way. There are two variables – the number of pixels available to be used and the number of operating colours. The RAM left over will be available for the user program. (The micro will also need some memory to operate the program.)

The more pixels (higher detail), the more memory will be used. The same is true for the number of colours. So you must choose the operating mode according to the type of image you wish to produce.

Micros generally have simple commands which allow you to move a point around the screen. You do this by inputting the co-ordinates to which you wish the point to go. Lines can be drawn from the new point to the previous one. (On some micros, lines are drawn by treating them as vectors.) Simple shapes are easily produced and, remember, all shapes can be drawn if you know how to draw a triangle – even a circle. You will quickly write short programs that let you produce shapes easily.

CHARACTER GRAPHICS

You can use the keyboard of a micro to display characters on the screen – lower case and upper case letters, numbers, punctuation marks etc. Each character fits into an eight by eight matrix of pixels. Specific pixels are 'turned on' to define each character as in the example below. Every character has an associated code number. This is its ASCII code number. The table of data for the standard character set is stored in ROM (computer's permanent memory). There are usually some spare ASCII code numbers, which you may use. You can define a new character and give it an ASCII code number. Your character can then be addressed by its code number. **User definable characters** are stored in RAM, so they are lost when you turn off the computer.

You could now make the Superman character appear anywhere on the screen, using the text commands. You can build up larger shapes, such as the Empire State building, from a series of grids as shown. Once you have mastered drawing shapes using character graphics, you will now want to make them move. Make Superman fly past the Empire State building. Do this by telling the computer to print the character, Superman in this case, at a particular point, then to 'unprint' it, only to print it again in the next position, and so on. Movement, or **animation**, can also be achieved by using colour changing techniques. This is explained in most manuals.

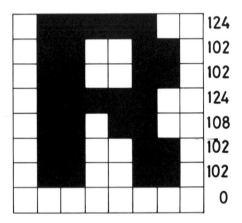

124
102
102
124
108
102
102
0

A new character can be defined using an eight by eight planning grid. You must tell the computer which pixels should be turned on in each row. The values for each row correspond to the 'byte' pattern. Each character is defined by eight values, each value being the sum of the required squares in each row. This is easy to understand if you follow the example of Superman shown below.

| 128 | 64 | 32 | 16 | 8 | 4 | 2 | 1 |

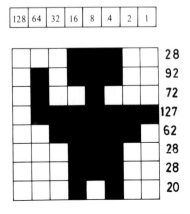

28
92
72
127
62
28
28
20

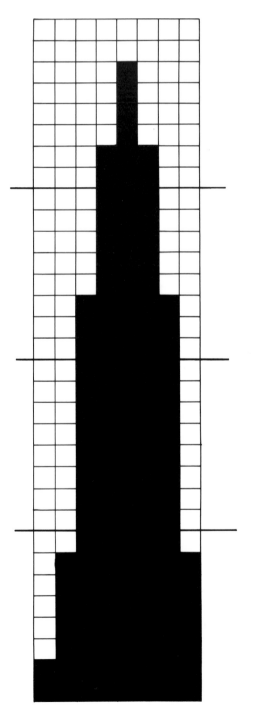

SOFTWARE

The range of software available for micros is growing all the time. A few programs have been specially written for computer aided design (CAD) in schools. Many of these programs carry out operations similar to those used commercially, but at a simpler level. Here are some examples of the types of programs you could run on your micro.

Solids of revolution

This type of program allows you to design shapes which have a circular cross-section. This is usually done by moving a cursor using the **direction keys**. Start by defining a profile which will then be mirror imaged to give a sectional view of the shape. The shape is then described as a solid object which you can revolve to obtain different views. You could use this program to design any object which is to be made on a wood or metal lathe, for example a handle for a tool, or a chesspiece.

Rotating 3-D images

It is a time-consuming task to draw an object from different viewpoints, so that you can visualize what it looks like from different directions. It is probably quicker to make a model or to model the object on a computer. The computer will be able to rotate it for you. However, it is often a lengthy task to define a shape and it may need a knowledge of co-ordinate geometry. Also, a lot of RAM is needed to run this type of program, so the images may have to be rather crude. Commercial programs are capable of continuous rotation (in real time), but on a micro the screen is blank between each view of the object being shown. A micro can produce such images in one-point perspective.

Statistical graphics

Raw statistics are difficult to understand, so it is often better to present them in a graphical form. **Line graphs**, **pie charts** and **histograms** are all types of data charts which can be drawn relatively quickly using a micro. You can produce very effective charts if you use the full colour potential. Unfortunately, for most of you, hardcopy will be black and white. One way of overcoming this is to take a photograph of the screen using a polaroid camera.

Drawing and draughting

There is a range of programs which lets you use the full graphics potential of your computer. These programs let you produce shapes such as triangles, rectangles, circles and ellipses, using only one or two commands. You can change the colours and fill the shapes with either brush (solid fill) or hatching. Often the **menu** (available commands) is displayed on the screen. You can produce detailed, high resolution graphics without spending hours programming.

CAD

More and more programs allow the micro to be used as an aid to designing. They may help you to carry out a drawing, such as the orthographic views of an object, or the design of a circuit. Usually a library of symbols is available and you can recall them and position them at will. Other programs carry out a particular task for you. For example, if a car designer designs the profile of a car, its drag coefficient and performance figures can be calculated by the computer. This type of program is a simple example of one way in which industry makes use of the computer.

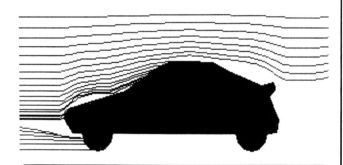

Drag coefficient=0.359

WIND TUNNEL SIMULATION

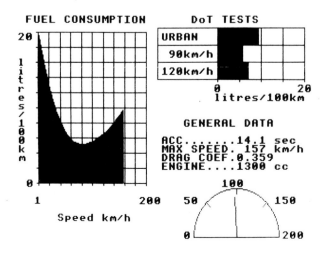

FUEL CONSUMPTION

DoT TESTS

URBAN

90km/h

120km/h

0   20
litres/100km

GENERAL DATA

ACC......14.1 sec
MAX SPEED. 157 km/h
DRAG COEF.0.359
ENGINE....1300 cc

Speed km/h

ROM extension

You can improve the graphics performance of most computers by increasing their ROM. This means increasing the micro's permanent memory. It is usually done by fitting an extra chip to the computer. A wide range of extra commands is then available for you. Here are some examples of extra commands.

TURTLE GRAPHICS is a method of producing intricate patterns using only the most straightforward commands. A 'turtle', usually a simple arrow, is moved around with commands such as 'Forward', 'Backward', 'Right' and 'Left'. As it moves it leaves a trail, a visual image, behind it.

TEXT allows text to be drawn in a range of sizes and colours. The style or **font** of the text can also be changed and it becomes possible to design your own character font.

SPRITE lets you define characters. A **sprite** is like the user definable character explained earlier, but larger (probably up to 24 × 24 dots). It can be moved easily about a screen and can be designed in a range of colours (depending on the computer and model).

PERSPECTIVE commands allow images to be created that take into account that in the real world objects foreshorten as they recede into the distance.

The precise commands available will vary depending on the particular ROM extension. Most extensions have a very wide range. Remember that these commands are also available if you use the right software. A ROM extension is far more convenient to use and it leaves RAM free for additional software and operating procedures.

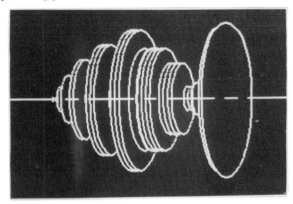

Did you know... CAD/CAM (computer aided design/manufacture) is revolutionizing the way things are designed and produced. The first application of the computer was as an automatic draughtsman. The computer was used to mimic a human being and to produce detailed drawings - not very creative, but quite important. Computers are absolutely precise. When humans made drawings of cars, for example, the right-hand side was always different from the left, because the drawings were inaccurate. Now with the aid of a computer, one side is the exact mirror image of the other.

The computer can be used to do things man cannot. *Three-dimensional modelling* lets you view anything, such as a car, a space shuttle, or the design for a shoe, from any angle. Depending on the complexity, objects can be rotated in real time. Images can also be scaled up and down, mirrored, exploded, twisted and have their colour changed at will.

Computers can also be used to work out the optimum layout of anything, from the road network of a new town to a manufacturing plant or the design of a silicon chip. This function is known as *routing*. Certain conditions are given to the computer and it produces the best solution every time.

Simulation is another technique which computers can carry out. A design engineer might, for example, model a North Sea oil rig on a computer and then subject it to a force 10 gale, to discover if the design will withstand such a buffeting. If it fails, he or she can then redesign it. Similarly, it is no longer necessary for car designers to crash cars into walls to discover how they will perform in an accident. Such tests can be carried out by simulation on the computer. Test performance can be improved with the information gained from simulation. In future, instead of the familiar 'back to the drawing board' when something does not work, we shall probably say, 'back to the terminal'!

Designers at work

All designers have to communicate ideas. Often they must draw and model to show a client a possible solution. They will also use sketches and drawings to develop their own ideas.

You have now learnt some of the basic techniques and skills of design and communication. The skills which you are beginning to master are similar to those which professional designers use. Designers shape the man-made world in which we live. Think of what needs to be designed - everything from advertisements to anoraks, from hospitals to helicopters and from videos to vases. Designers obviously have to specialize in particular aspects of design. Some specialist designers have special names - a person who designs houses, for example, is called an **architect**.

Design, as you have probably discovered, is not easy. Even when you are designing and making something for your personal use, it is tricky to get it just right. Imagine how much more difficult it is to design a hospital, which will be used by thousands of people for up to one hundred years, or a helicopter which cannot afford to fail even once, without leading to disaster. Because of the complexity of projects of this type, they are usually the work of teams of designers, with groups responsible for specific aspects.

Designers work in a wide range of disciplines. In the field of engineering design there are mechanical, electrical, electronic, civil, chemical, aeronautical, marine and production engineers. Designers in these areas are responsible for the performance of a wide range of technical products. The world of communications offers tremendous scope to designers. They create, for example, sets and costumes for theatre and television, whilst graphic designers work on books, magazines, advertisements, packaging and trademarks.

This next section of the book describes the work of six designers in relation to a design project with which they have been involved. You will see that these designers have used all the techniques to which you have been introduced. Success in design, even for professionals, does not come easily. It requires perspiration, inspiration and often a degree of luck as well.

ARCHITECTURE

Roderick Ham is an architect specializing in the design of theatres. The drawings on this page were his response to a brief to design an Arts Centre that included an auditorium, for a local authority. Several architects were interviewed to begin with and asked to show examples of their work. Roderick's approach was chosen and he was asked to develop a design. This meant he had to establish the concept of the building, the relationship between the various spaces and the character of the building. These drawings were produced to communicate his ideas to the clients.

The drawings are typical of those any architect might produce. The first is a ground floor plan. It shows the layout of the various spaces. A plan view has to be produced for each floor. The next drawing is an example of a cross-section through the building. Several sections are necessary to show the relationship between the various floors of the building. Sections and plans describe how the building functions and operates.

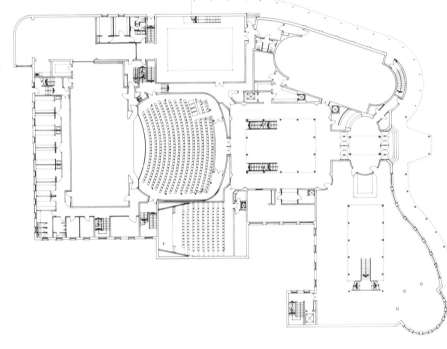

Elevations describe how the building will look. They are drawn straight on like plans and, for convenience, are referred to by their approximate relation to the points of the compass. The character of the building is evident from the elevations. From these it is possible to imagine the visual impact it will have on the surrounding area.

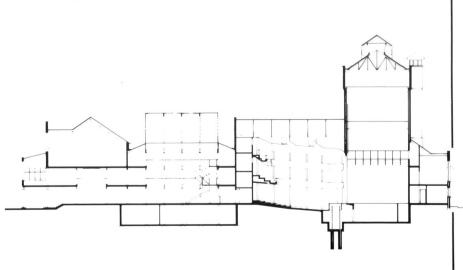

Elevations, plans and sections are all two-dimensional drawings. The architect also needs pictorial views. These may be perspectives, or a cut away axonometric drawing, as in this case. You will remember that this system is often used by architects, because it can be projected from a plan view. This drawing allows you to 'walk through the building'. It gives a good idea of what the building looks like. It is also an excellent reference drawing, enabling someone to appreciate the relationships between the more detailed drawings.

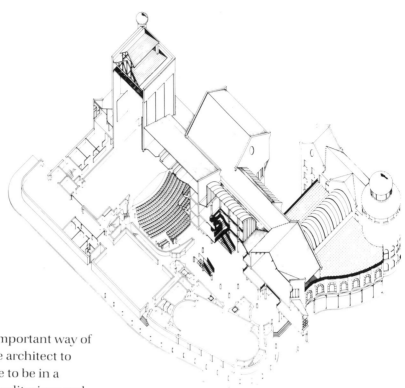

Atmospheric sketches are also an important way of communicating ideas. They allow the architect to convey to someone what it will be like to be in a building or, in this case, to sit in the auditorium and watch a play.

Finally he produced a model – a scaled down three-dimensional representation of the building. For those unfamiliar with architectural drawings, this is the most valuable communication tool. You can walk round it, select your own viewing point and gain an intimate understanding of the architect's vision. Roderick set out to design a building for the Arts, one which would be rich in visual interest, reflecting the variety of activities which might take place inside. You can decide for yourself if you think he succeeded. It took him three months of intensive work to produce this submission, and the drawings were only a small part of it. If approved, it will be back to the drawing board to carry out all the necessary detailed designing.

INTERIOR DESIGN

Every year airports become busier as more and more people fly from country to country. New airports have to be built, existing airports expanded and inefficient facilities modernized to cope with the increased demand. Heathrow airport, London, is one of the largest airports in the world, 11 million people pass through terminal 3 alone every year. A new terminal will soon be completed to help cope with the continual increase in passengers. Even with this extra capacity it is predicted that by 1990 terminal 3 will once again be handling 11 million people. During the next few years, while there is spare capacity, the British Airports Authority (BAA) is going to take the opportunity to refurbish terminal 3.

Angela Simpson is an interior designer working for Fitch and Company, one of the largest design consultancies in Europe. Angela is co-ordinating the major refurbishment of terminal 3. The project will take several years to complete as the terminal must continue to function smoothly while building work is being carried out. The designing and planning phase will take from two to three years. Construction is scheduled to start in April 1986 but it will not be completed until the early 1990s.

This is a highly complex operation and many architects, designers and planners will be involved. The project started with the BAA briefing a firm of architects, D.Y. Davies and Associates, on their requirements for the revamped terminal. Simply put, their brief was to dress up an old building to make it fit for the 21st century. The architects' responsibility is for structural changes, the new facade and extensions which will increase the overall floor space. A major objective is to improve traffic flow through the terminal, both passenger and baggage. To achieve this, the one vertical circulation point will be replaced by five escalators. This will greatly improve access between the two levels, relieving congestion and allowing more passengers to use the terminal.

Once the main structure of the building was resolved, Angela and her team set about designing the interior. There are three aspects to this:
1   Functional, block plans and flow diagrams are used to establish passenger flow-through for both arrivals and departures.
2   Aesthetic, pictorial visualizations will help to determine the atmosphere within the terminal.
3   Facilities, block plans, visuals and concept graphics will be used to plan the shopping mall and the food court.

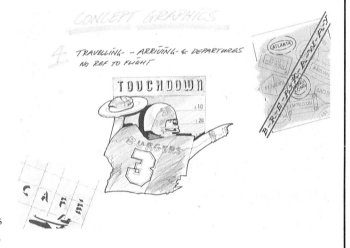

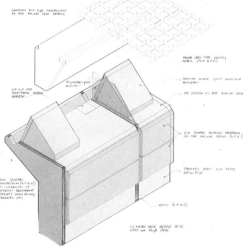

BAA INFORMATION DESK + SIGNAGE

The first step is to agree the concept for the scheme. The designers will present their ideas to the project team. The team includes BAA project and terminal management, the BAA design manager, Jane Priestman and the architects. Image boards and sample boards are shown to the client. These consist of photographs of existing environments and samples of what materials might be used. The client's reaction to these will help the designers discover what is really required. There will be many meetings and presentations before an agreement is reached. The concept wil be visualized in high quality one-point perspectives with plans showing spatial arrangements and movements.

The chosen concept is then reviewed by the design committee of the BAA. Their approval and authorization of expenditure signals the next phase, when more detailed planning will take place. The terminal must withstand the constant battering it will receive from millions of passengers. Fittings must be robust and the finish resilient to such things as impact damage, cigarette burns and general wear and tear. Materials with proven qualities will generally be used, but some research and development will be carried out into new materials.

The design team aims to create an interior which is cool, calm and efficient. The predominant colour will be grey, achieving a neutral backdrop on which other colours and textures can be used to create focal points. The check-in system and baggage handling will have a high-tech image, and all aspects will be computer controlled. Items such as check-in counters will be drawn accurately. Models and prototypes will be made to check that every detail is correct before final construction takes place.

Passenger facilities for this terminal are on the upper floor. The shopping area has been designed with a high street feel, lively and more colourful than the passenger halls. The food court must cater for a wide range of tastes and a number of concepts and block plans will be explored before the final decision is taken. Sketched perspectives are used as these communicate the feel and atmosphere far better than rigid drawing styles. These facilities must be well designed as it is the profit they generate which will help to pay for the whole scheme.

When the designing is almost complete, the work will soon be put out to tender. Builders, engineers, shop fitters, decorators and many others will take the designers' drawings and turn them into reality. The design team hope to be involved during the construction phase to ensure that their ideas and concepts will eventually satisfy the whims and needs of the international travellers of the 21st century.

The American Cafe 2

COMPUTER GRAPHICS

Computers have made a new and exciting world of visual images possible. It takes vision, imagination and the skill of a designer to realize the computer's full potential. Jilly Knight is the senior animator at Electronic Arts, a company that specializes in computer animation.

The title sequence for Sportsnight was a joint venture between Jilly and the BBC's senior graphics designer, Darrell Pockett. Between them they set out to create the first title sequence produced completely by computer graphics. The first step was for Darrell to produce the **storyboard**, which is a series of drawings outlining the images wanted in the sequence.

The plan was to show a number of moving images connected with the sports featured in the programme: a racing car, an athletics shoe, a snooker ball, a football etc. This would start with a flight over a futuristic city, finishing by zooming in on a sports stadium, as the programme titles appeared. It was the task of the animators to turn this idea into the sequence which you may have seen on television.

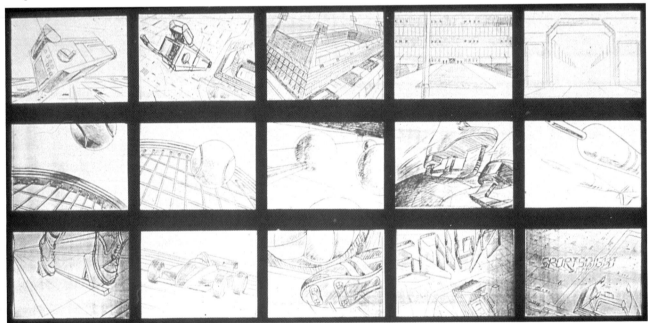

They had to decide on the sports. A variety of objects were modelled in a simple form on the computer. Those which produced the best visual images were chosen. The computer images were built up from detailed drawings, which showed exact shape, size and colour. The drawings shown here follow through the story of one object, the dart. As well as the detail drawing, others were made to describe the path of the dart as it moved across the screen.

From the drawings, the dart was turned into a computer model. This was in the form of strings of numbers. A single screen, full of numbers, represents about one-fifteenth of the total listing needed for the dart alone. Once the computer knew enough about the dart, it could move it in any direction at the required speed.

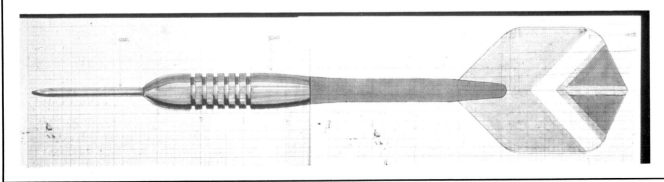

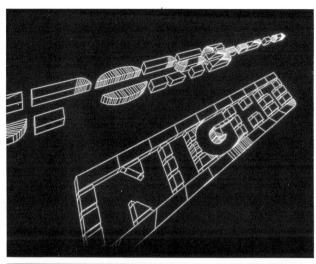

When all the images had been stored in the computer, individual sequences were produced. These were recorded on 35 mm film. The final animation was produced from these shots at a speed of 25 frames per second. A section of the dart sequence is shown at the foot of the page. The dart sequence lasts for five seconds, so altogether 125 separate images were needed. Each element of the title was built up in this way.

The final views of the town and stadium required a great deal of planning. For example, the plan of the town was designed and drawn by an architect, and the stadium and programme title were made as real 3-D models. All of these drawings and models were needed as visual references from which Jilly and the other animators could work.

The last stage was to add the music. As a result, some shots had to be rearranged. Finally, after much planning, designing and modification, the title sequence was approved by the client, the BBC, and was given the go-ahead for transmission. The bulk of the work had been carried out during a period of intensive activity lasting over two months; the final product lasts just 40 seconds.

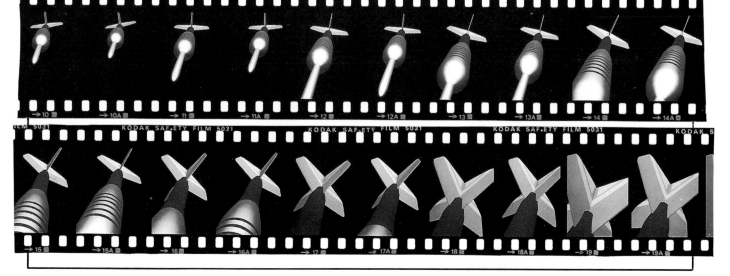

INDUSTRIAL DESIGN

What does a company do when its product is the market leader in a highly competitive area and the potential for future growth appears limited? One answer is 'to diversify the company's product base', or in other words, to start making other things. Duracell, makers of long life, alkaline, sealed cell batteries, decided to do just that. If the new product were also powered by batteries, potentially increased profits would come from two sources – the new product and increased battery sales.

This was a new venture for Duracell, so they decided to seek advice from a design consultancy. They selected BIB, a consultancy specializing in Industrial Design. Nick Butler was one of the team of four which spent 14 months designing and developing the new product.

A range of ideas was generated with one thing in common – all the products would require batteries for power. A number of the ideas had real potential and many may be developed in the future. The design team chose to start by designing a torch. The designers knew that an original concept was essential in a competitive market. Two hundred torches were assessed. They could largely be described as cylindrical, the shape being dictated by the batteries. The designers were struck by an obvious thought: as the torches were round, they would roll when put on a flat surface. Torches are only used in the dark, so if they have to be hand held, only one hand is left free. This makes tasks doubly difficult! A design concept started to develop – a torch which would stand on a surface and be capable of directing a beam of light to an exact spot. At this early stage of development, ideas were explored using drawings such as the one shown.

Traditional torches often corrode around the switch contacts. An elegant solution to overcome this defect was produced. The switch could be incorporated into the variable angle light source. This would result in a single operating action. The swivel top would turn the light source on and off and allow it to be set at specific angles. Additionally, the lens and bulb would be protected when the torch was not in use. These ideas were explored using models, essential when functional operations have to be designed.

Good ideas have to be made to work and the switch concept proved to be a thorny problem. The contacts had to be located in the swivel and they had to work every time. The contacts used in current torches were tried, but the material proved to be too soft. Frequent failure occurred. The solution did not come quickly, but eventually the design team tried using a base metal, tin, for the contacts and it worked every time. The contacts were moulded into the pivot and were designed to give a positive feel to the switch and 15 positions for the light source. The switch was set up in a test rig and was still operating without failure after $3\frac{1}{2}$ million cycles!

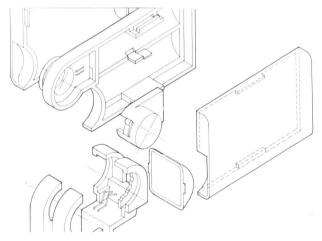

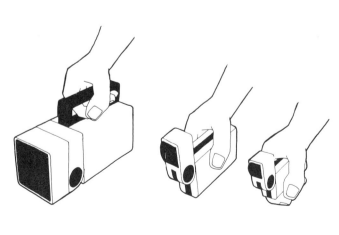

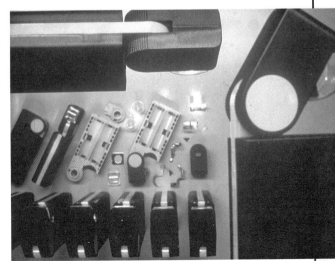

The visual appearance of the torch was vital to its success. A crisp, futuristic image was chosen. Black seemed the obvious colour for the plastic moulding. The main structural element, the spine of the torch, had to be stable and non-reactive. An acetal resin moulding would have all these properties, but this polymer is only available in a limited range of colours, which does not include black. Yellow was chosen for this element. It provides a strong contrast to the black casing and a powerful corporate image, which will be used on all future Duracell products. The final prototypes confirmed that Nick and the design team had designed a new concept for a torch, pleasant to handle, attractive to look at, simple to operate and providing an accurate, adjustable focused beam.

When the design was finalized, each component was drawn in detail. A general arrangement drawing was made to show how the parts fitted together. The design was developed using drawings and models to clarify and give form to ideas and to communicate ideas to the client, and finally to the company responsible for making the die moulds and manufacturing the torch.

When designers approach a project with fresh minds, innovative solutions should result. Good design also sells. In the first two years, several million Durabeam torches were sold, each containing one or two Duracell batteries.

AUTOMOBILE DESIGN

The major car manufacturers are all household names: Ford, Vauxhall, Honda, Volkswagen and Renault, for example. The design consultancies which undertake projects for the larger manufacturers are less well known. In Italy, there are several internationally known independent design houses. In the UK, there are only one or two with similar reputations. Ogle Design is one of these. Ogle undertakes work in a number of areas related to transport design. The head of transport design at Ogle is Ron Saunders, a specialist in car design, who previously worked for Ford.

Designing a new car from scratch is a long process. It can take from three to six years, which is not surprising as there are over 7000 individual components in a modern car. Ogle is currently involved in a project to design a car for the year 2000, only 15 years away. Predictions had to be made about the needs of the driver in the next century. The Ogle team investigated passenger comfort. As a result, they made the seating position higher, so that the cushion height would be similar to that of a proper lounge chair. Putting passengers upright also creates more room fore and aft for storage. Engineering decisions also had to be considered. The family run-around of the year 2000 is based on a four cylinder transverse engine. By then, the designers expect the power train to be smaller without a loss in performance.

Once Ron's team had a grasp of the problem, they started to produce sketches and felt marker drawings of how they thought the car would look. Car designers are highly skilled in marker drawings. They can quickly produce dramatic visuals of a car's appearance. As the design team continued work, the car began to take shape. It would need to be aerodynamically efficient, with smooth contours. The designers are also working on a range of movable aerodynamic devices. These may improve braking, by introducing systems similar to those used in aircraft, and increase the stability of the vehicle in the face of cross winds. Increased stability is important if lighter materials, such as plastics, are used in preference to metal. A novel feature of the proposed vehicle is the use of gull wing doors at the rear. These greatly improve access and help maintain the lines of the car.

With many problems solved on paper, the next step was to make a model. Models were made in clay to start with, as this is a material which can be modelled easily yet with great accuracy. A prototype one-third full size was made in glass reinforced plastic. This model was used to test public reaction and help clarify ideas about the vehicle's appearance. The model was tested in a wind-tunnel. A drag factor (Cd) of 0.27 was established, an excellent figure.

Ron's team had done a great deal of hard work, to get to this stage, but the car is still only a concept. If it were to be manufactured, there is still much design work to be done. We shall have to wait and see the outcome of this project. These drawings may well be a glimpse of the future. This car may be the one you will be driving in twenty years' time.

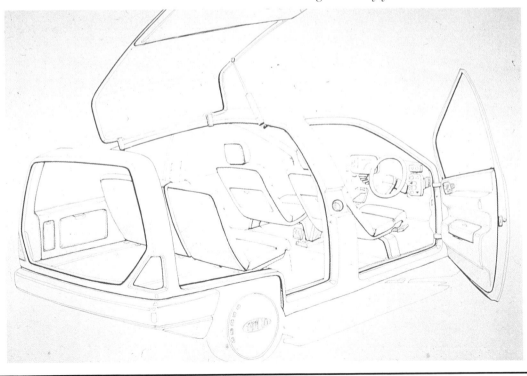

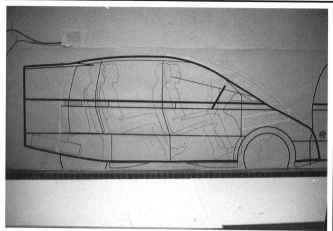
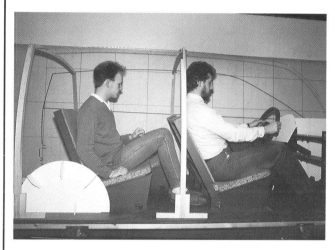

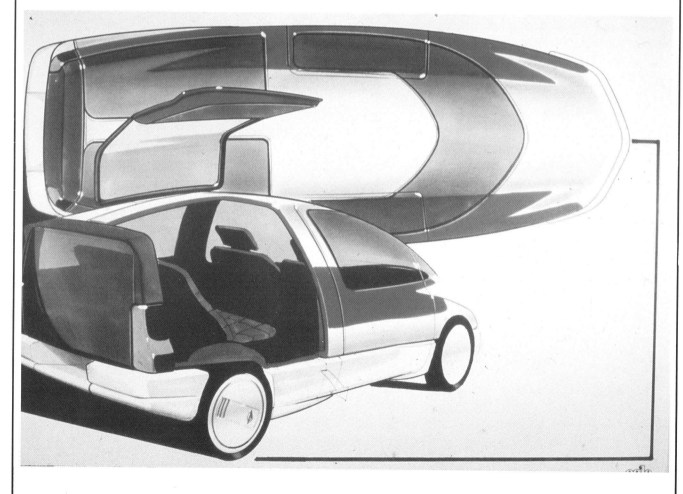

GRAPHICS/PACK DESIGN

Designers in the field of packaging work in many ways. They are usually commissioned by a company to produce a new design or to update an existing one. Alternatively, they will identify a package which might be improved in some way, redesign it and approach the manufacturer with their suggestion. **Speculative** design like this can sometimes be an important method of generating work. Trevor Crocker is a partner in the Pack Design Company which, as its name suggests, is a company specializing in design packaging.

A leading confectioner decided to produce a chocolate lemon in addition to its very successful chocolate orange. When a company decides to capitalize on a successful product in this way, it is known as a **line extension**.

The designers thought that this would be a good opportunity to investigate the possibility of designing a new pack suitable for both products. The construction would have to be structurally strong to protect the product and simple to produce, make up and fill. It would also combine effective visual appeal and display at the point of sale (POS).

The first step involved cardboard engineering – designing for the pack. They sketched out their first thoughts in very rough form, generally referred to as 'scamps', and considered many ideas for shapes and construction.

They then modelled the most promising ideas in card. They developed the most practical design into a blank prototype. As you can see, it consists of an open-ended box, with crimped corners and two flat card inserts to hold the product.

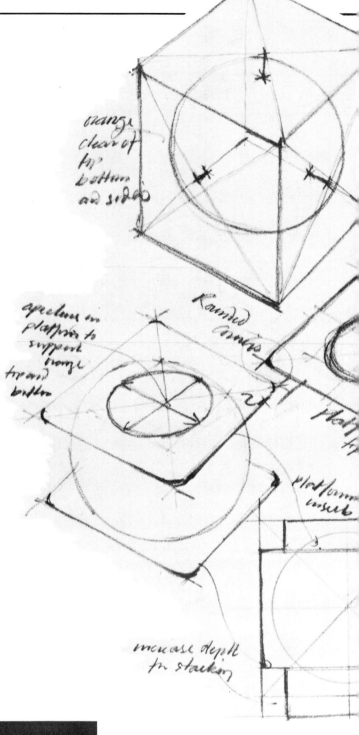

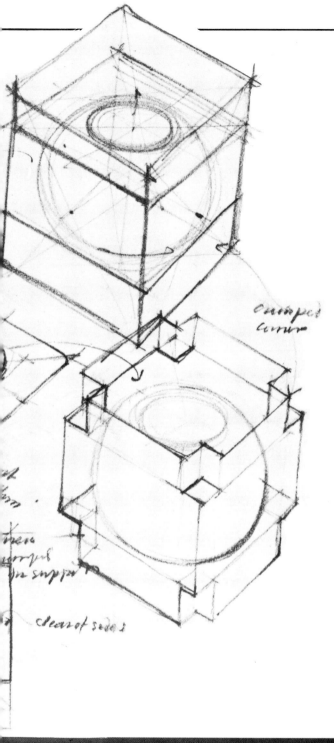

The construction had been designed to help speed up the filling and packing operation as follows: bottom corners crimped, base card inserted, chocolate fruit placed in position, top card placed on product, top corners crimped. There was an additional advantage. As the base crimping was slightly smaller than the top, the boxes could be interlocked economically for transit, and stacked safely within sensible limits at the point of sale.

The construction completed, work could now begin on the exterior graphics. The pack has two sides pierced with a circular aperture to reveal the contents. The two remaining sides carry all the information about the product. They decided to illustrate the product in two ways. On one side, the contents would be shown completely wrapped. On the other side, an unwrapped view would show the individual segments.

'Scamps' were produced using felt markers showing four colourways to distinguish one flavour from another. They chose red and blue, already associated with plain and milk chocolate, for the established chocolate orange, and citrus green and yellow for the new chocolate lemon.

They worked the 'scamps' up into finished roughs in the form of 'concept' boards. These are flat two-dimensional impressions of how the packs will finally appear.

Finally, they produced complete three-dimensional full colour dummies for presentation to the company.

The response by the company after assessing the appearance and the feasibility of producing the new packaging designs was favourable. Many advantages were identified. However, despite the attractions of the new design, the company decided to keep its original packing, which was already established in the market place.

In this instance, the speculative design was not accepted. This sometimes happens, but designers need to take such risks to generate work. When work is commissioned by a client, the process can take a long time. Designer and client have to agree on the right image for the product, for it is through the packaging that the image will be shown. If the designer gets it right, then the packaging becomes a very valuable tool in increasing sales of the product. Even an excellent product can fail if it is not well marketed. Designers like Trevor ensure that the product is enhanced by its packaging and presented to the customer in the best possible way.

Projects

1 INVESTIGATION

You can learn a great deal by looking at and copying drawings made by others. This project is a continuous one. It is to make a collection of drawings which you come across in papers, colour supplements, magazines, advertising material etc. Make your collection in a folder or scrapbook. The collection must be arranged in categories, to be of any use to you. Here are some suggestions:

1 Designers' sketches – freehand drawings of ideas

2 Orthographic drawings – ones showing only two dimensions of an object

3 Paraline drawings – 3-D drawings, where lines indicating length and width are parallel, such as in isometric and axonometric views

4 Perspective drawings – one, two or three-point perspective

5 Technical views – drawings showing internal details of an object, probably sectional or exploded views

6 Presentation drawings – designers' drawings that have been fully rendered in colour to give a realistic impression of how an object will look

7 Corporate identity graphics – company logos and the various ways in which a company might use its logo

8 Information graphics – signs, symbols, pictograms and any examples where a graphic image is used instead of words

9 Statistical graphics – pictorial statistics, graphs, pie charts, histograms, where the image helps you to understand the figures

10 Explanation graphics – drawings that tell you how to do something

11 Natural objects – always useful as a design resource

12 Old cards – many Christmas and birthday cards have excellent graphic images

You will probably think of other categories as well. Until you have covered certain sections of the book, some drawings may be difficult to index. Put them to one side until you know how to categorize them.

Also look carefully at drawings you cannot collect. Everywhere you go, you are being bombarded with graphics. Walk along your local high street and you will see what I mean.

Television is another medium which uses graphics extensively. A television screen is flat, 2-D, yet we view through it a solid 3-D world. It is worth observing how solid images are flattened out by the television and yet still appear solid. Look at the televised snooker game. The snooker balls are spheres and that is how we see them, but on the flat screen they are really discs. Look carefully and see how this is achieved. You will soon find other similar examples.

If your school has a video camera, you can use it to flatten out 3-D objects. This can make them easier to draw, because the foreshortening has been calculated. The photograph here shows how this is achieved.

Remember to use your eyes to look at other drawings and to see how they achieve the desired effect.

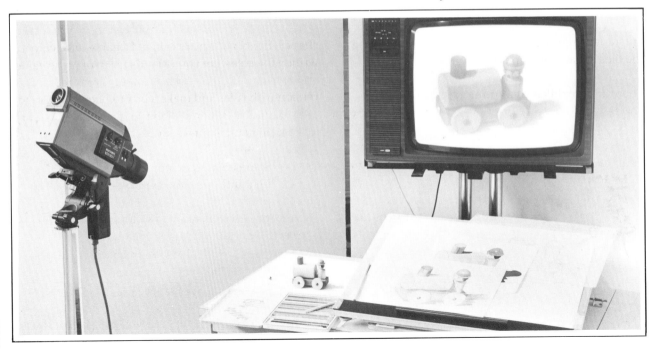

2   POLYOMINOES

You have probably heard of, and played, dominoes. Have you heard of polyominoes? A **domino** is a special polyomino. A domino is a shape made up of two squares. It is a rectangle. A shape composed of one square is a **monomino**. Does it begin to make sense? Omino – a square; monomino – one square; domino – two squares; **polyomino** – a shape made up of any number of squares. 'Poly' means 'many', as in polygon – a shape made up of any number of sides. A shape composed of three squares is a **tromino**, four squares a **tetromino**, five squares a **pentomino**, and so on.

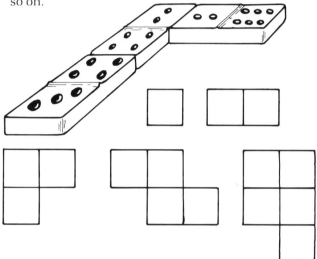

Polyominoes are interesting shapes. Before you can use them, you must discover a little more about them.

A tromino can be formed in two different ways – a rectangle or an L shape. The L shape is interesting. If you had a tile that shape, it would tessellate on a surface to produce a wide variety of patterns. Design three different patterns based on an L-shaped tromino, either by using squared paper or by cutting out paper shapes. Produce your patterns assuming the tiles are available in two colours.

There are five different tetrominoes. Two are fairly obvious – a square made up of four smaller squares and a large rectangle. Can you find the other three? Choose one of these three and produce a tiling pattern, in the same way as you did with the tromino.

Here is a real challenge. There are 12 different pentominoes – shapes made up of five monominoes. Start by finding these shapes.

These 12 shapes are made up of 60 separate monominoes (12 × 5), not quite enough to cover a chess-board, which has 64 squares. To cover the board you will need a tetromino, use the one which is still a square.

Cut the twelve pentominoes and the single tetromino out of some stiff card. Make the shapes so that a single monomino is the same size as a single square on a chess-board. Now solve this puzzle with the 13 card pieces and a chess-board. The object is to cover completely the board with the 13 polyomino shapes. It is quite difficult, but you should succeed as there are estimated to be at least 100 000 different solutions to this problem!

As the number of squares in a polyomino increases, so does the number of arrangements. There are, for example, 35 hexominoes (six squares) and 108 heptominoes (seven squares).

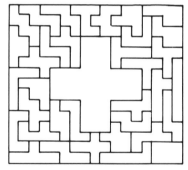

Now you are an expert in polyominoes, see if you can design a game based around some of these interesting shapes. When you have designed a game, take care in writing the rules. Let your friends try to play the game and modify it until it works. Produce a finished version with rules and make a box to pack it in. Try to make a prototype model of the game – what it would look like if manufactured and put on sale.

Here are some ideas to explore.

1   Put patterns on the surface – jigsaw type of game.
2   Two people lay shapes alternately on a board until one cannot go.
3   Shapes or numbers are linked up as in dominoes.
4   Turn the squares into cubes, so that the game is 3-D rather than 2-D.
5   A puzzle game played by one person, but with different possible solutions.

3 ANIMATION

Making images is a challenge that has been tackled in many ways during the last 200 years. The magic lantern led to the kinematograph and the start of the motion picture industry. Now videos can record and immediately replay the past.

Moving pictures rely on a discovery made in 1825 – 'The Persistence of Vision'. It was found that if a number of images can be observed at the right speed, the eye cannot detect the separate drawings, but combines them into one moving picture. A number of interesting and novel devices were invented during the nineteenth century, to entertain and to charm. The mechanical magic lantern is still fun, even if it is rather simplistic beside Walt Disney's Tron and the computer animated images which are becoming so familiar. Here are a number of simple projects, which start with Victorian devices and lead up to animating computer images.

1   A **thaumatrope** is like a coin spinning on its edge. It can be made from a piece of card with strings attached on either side, or with the card fixed to a piece of dowel as shown. A visual image is split, so that part appears on one side and the second part on the other side. When the disc is spun at speed, the two images merge into one. Make a simple card thaumatrope. You may even think of some other devices using this principle.

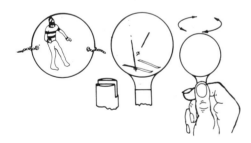

2   A **zoetrope** is a drum which can be spun on a spindle. Inside the drum there are a series of sequenced drawings. These are viewed through a number of slots in the top half of the drum. When the drum is spinning, the images coincide and appear to move.

You can make a zoetrope from scrap material. You will need the polypropylene base from a large PET bottle for the drum, the measure from a large bottle of fabric conditioner (or similar) as a base, a drawing pin and some flexible card. The drawing shows you how they are assembled.

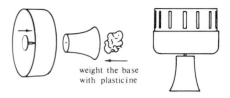

weight the base
with plasticine

Next make the two developments from the card, as shown. When they have been glued, they can be put inside the drum. You can try out your zoetrope and see if the ball bounces. Try drawing some more sequences and see if they work. You may wish to design and make an improved version of the device as well.

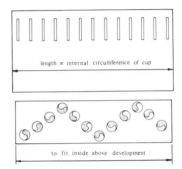

length = internal circumference of cup

to fit inside above development

3   **Flicker books** are old devices. They have been in production since 1868. You have probably made simple versions on the edge of an exercise book. Take an A3 sheet of flexible card (the front cover of an A3 layout pad will do) and divide it into 21 similar rectangles – seven along the length and three up the height. Draw a spinning disc on this flicker book. You will see the layout for this drawing on the opposite page. Cut out and assemble your coloured drawings. The simplest method is to use double-sided tape. When all the sheets are together, squeeze them into a vice or press.

A flicker book can also be produced using a computer. The sequence on the lower half of the opposite page was produced with a program which allowed 3-D objects to be drawn in perspective, rotated and also enlarged or reduced. Each image was printed as hardcopy and then cut out, mounted on card, coloured and turned into a flicker book. If you have the facilities, try making a computer flicker book.

4   Use character graphics or sprites to produce a short **computer animated sequence**. You will find the listing to do this in your computer manual. Once you can make something move, you should be able to devise a simple game.

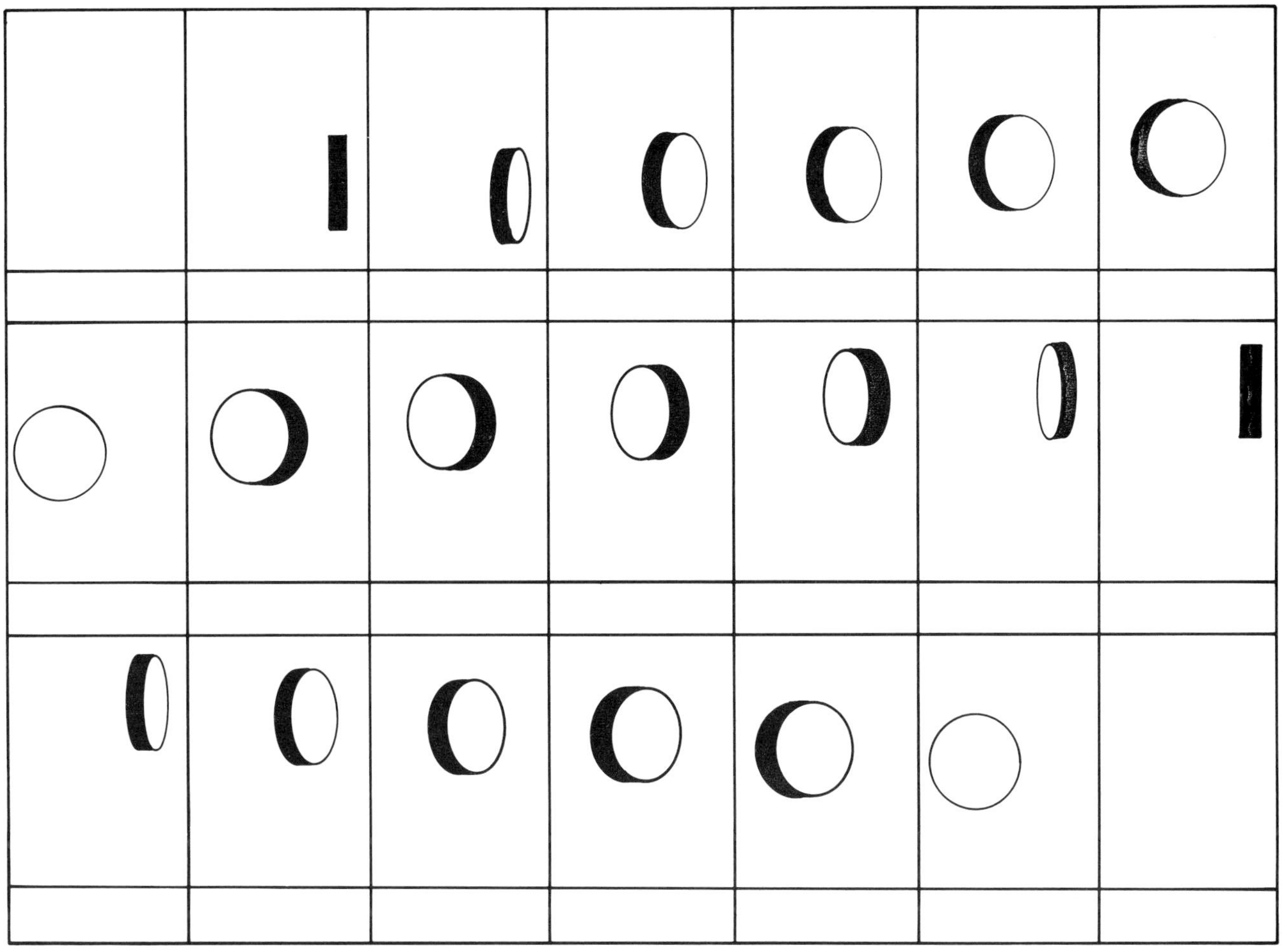

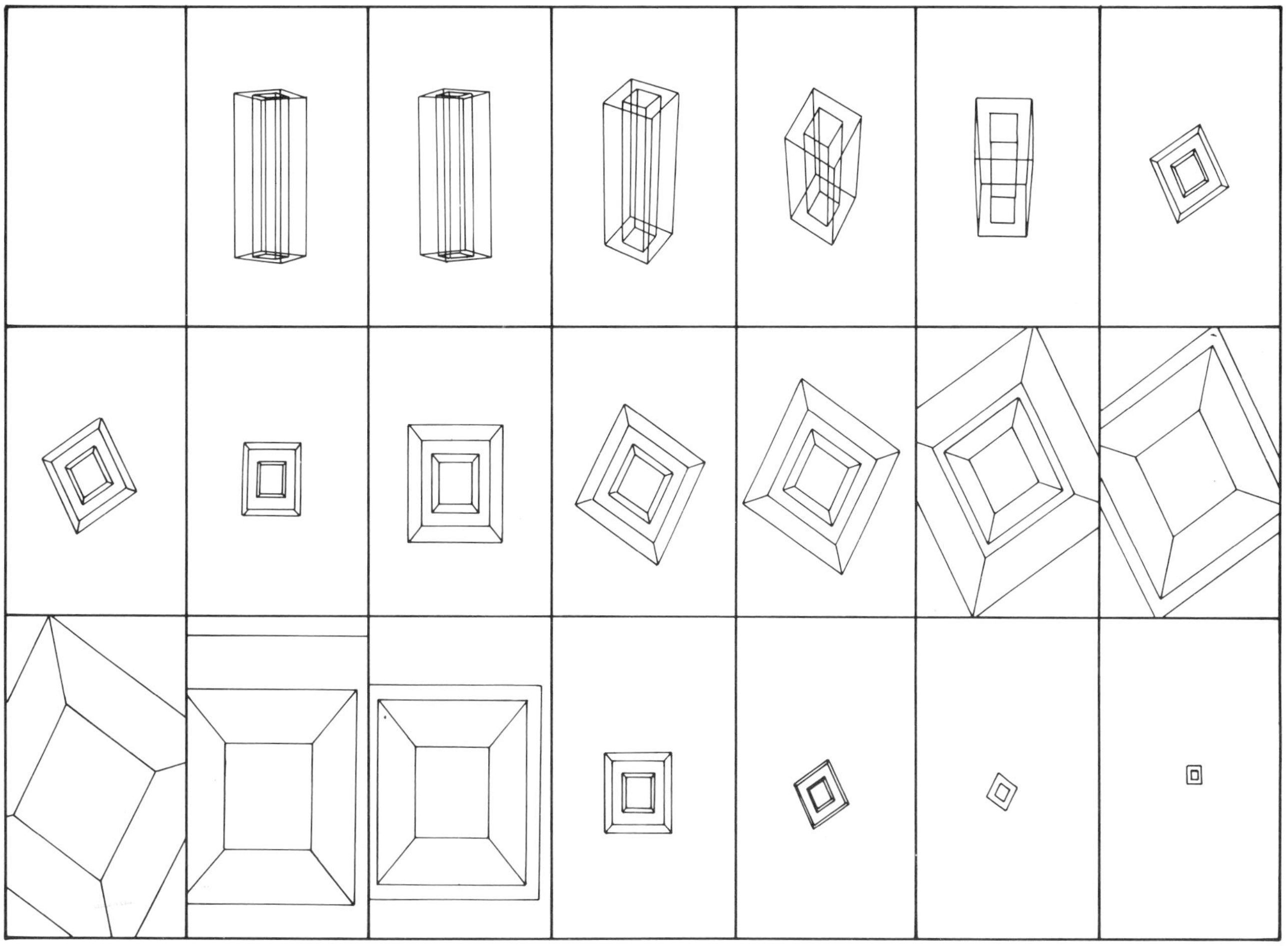

4 ILLUSION

Many of the images we create in graphics are attempts to deceive the eye. For example, drawings of solid objects on flat sheets of paper are a deception. Some artists have produced drawings which attempt to confound the eye. This project will show you how to draw some confusing images, whilst at the same time practising some of the drawing systems with which you are now familiar.

1 **Axonometric projection**
This figure is known as **Thiéry's figure**. Construct it as shown. When you have drawn it, notice how first one part will appear solid and then as an empty corner, then the original view is reversed. You can also view it as a rather peculiar figure consisting of two solids.

2 **Isometric projection**   Here are two isometric drawings which create confusion. They are both based on six equidistant parallel lines. Draw them as shown.

3 **Oblique projection**   This is a drawing system you have not used before. It is, however, very simple. Start by drawing a front elevation. Project lines at 45° from all corners. Mark the width off along these lines and complete the view. This is known as **Schröder's reversible staircase**. Can you see why?

4 **One-point perspective**
Construct the interior view of a corridor as shown. Once you have the interior, place equal size objects, such as the outline of a person, at different points. What appears to happen to the images?

Try this shading exercise to create another illusion. This is a **brightness illusion**. Produce an even grey tone in the strip in the centre of the box. With care, add a tone in the top and bottom portions which goes from dark on the left to light on the right. What do you notice now about the even grey tone through the centre?

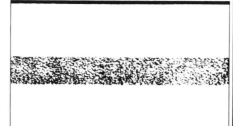

M.C. Escher was an artist famous for illusions. You may have seen some of his drawings (usually lithographs). The drawing to the right is a simplified version of his impossible waterfall. It is drawn in isometric projection. See if you can copy the drawing.

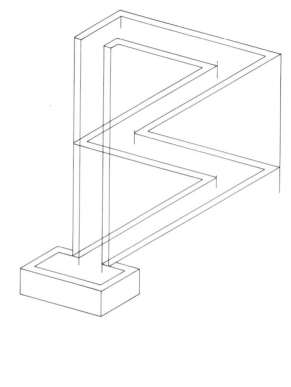

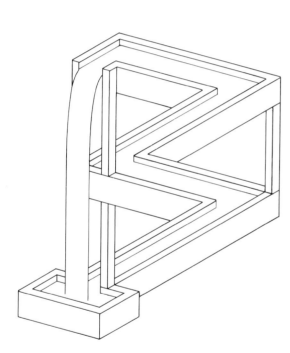

Carry out some research at your school and local libraries. See if you can find any more information about, and examples of, optical illusions. Make a collection of the images you find. Use your collection as a resource for the following design brief.

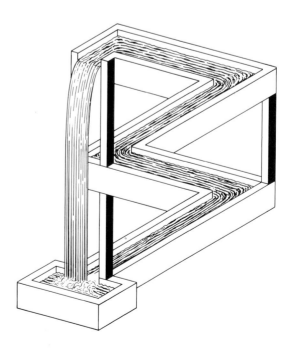

Brief A petrol company has decided to give a drinks mat with every 30 litres of petrol, as part of a promotional campaign. There will be ten mats in the set. Each mat is to have a different optical illusion on it. Design the set of mats and make a model of one mat using acrylic, coloured paper and either transparent contact film or clear resin. The acrylic should be white with a maximum of two other colours used. Fine drawing tapes can be used to produce lines on acrylic.

5 MAKE YOUR OWN EQUIPMENT

Earlier in this book, you were asked to make your own templates (Activity 46). Here are some ideas for other items of graphic equipment you could make.

Perspective drawing boards

To make a simple one-point perspective board, all you need is an A3 sheet of stiff card. Mark out an arc of a circle as shown. Mark the arc using something like a large dinner plate (about 240 mm diameter). Cut carefully along the line with a craft knife. If possible, use the object you drew around as a template for cutting. Next, cut a 10 mm slice off the bottom of the card. This now needs to be glued to the corner piece, so that it would, if extended, pass through the centre of the arc. This can be done by drawing a chord and constructing the perpendicular bisector. This part now forms the **perspective line generator**. Move it carefully in the arc and all lines drawn along the long edge will pass through a single vanishing point, the centre of the circle.

If you cut an arc in an identical position on the other top corner, you will have a board which will enable you to draw two-point perspectives. The previous board is not very adaptable as the vanishing point is fixed. This perspective board requires a little more time and care to make, but it is more useful.

You will need a sheet of material 420 mm long by 380 mm high. Strong cardboard will do, but it will not be very durable. Hardboard, polystyrene sheet or acrylic will last longer. Cut off three 12 mm wide lengths 420 mm long. This must be done very accurately, so ask your teacher to do it on a band saw, or with a circular saw. Cut one of these lengths exactly in half, giving two pieces 210 mm long. Mark these four pieces and the remaining part of the board as shown.

The points marked are positions for holes. Look at the completed board, as shown, and you will see that pins are needed. The pins pass through these holes allowing the two elements being joined freedom to rotate. Press studs work very well, but there are many other possibilities. Do not drill the holes until you have decided what pins you will use. This board gives you 25 different vanishing points from which to choose. There are still some practical problems left to solve. Make sure that you have sorted these out before you start to make the board.

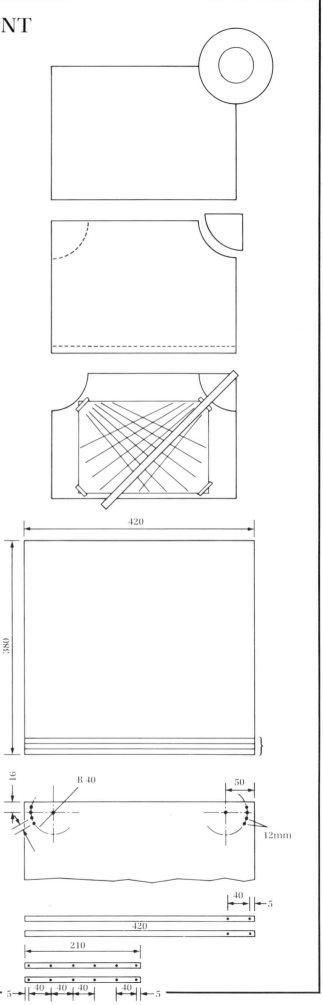

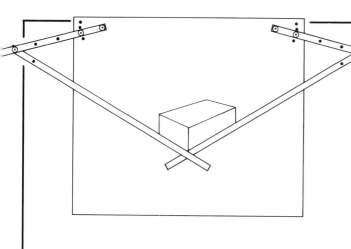

When you use the board, make sure the two swinging arms are in the same position. Start by drawing a 50 mm sided cube from each pair of vanishing points. Use these drawings to make a chart for future reference.

There are many other types of perspective drawing boards. Maybe you can design one that is simpler and more versatile?

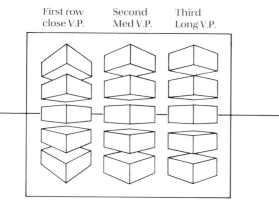

First row close V.P. Second Med V.P. Third Long V.P.

Pantograph

You will remember that this is a device for enlarging or reducing drawings. You should be able to design and make one of your own by looking at the given diagrams. There are several points to bear in mind.

1 All joints must be free to rotate.
2 Point A must be secured to the drawing surface.
3 For enlarging, the pencil goes in C and the tracer point is B. For reduction, these two points are reversed.
4 DEFB is always a parallelogram.
5 Points D and F should be capable of being moved to other positions to change the scale of the reduction or enlargement.
6 Point E should be supported but allowed to glide over the paper.

Design and make a pantograph which will enlarge or reduce in the ratios 1:2, 1:3 and 1:5. Find the positions of the various holes using card and drawing pin models.

Light box

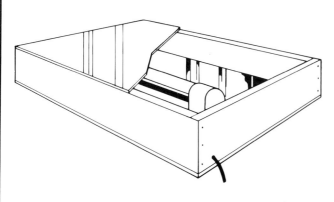

A simple light box can be made using a Thorn 2D bulb. It is powerful enough to cope with A4 drawings. Make a cabinet to contain the bulb. Make the lid out of white opaque acrylic. Design all the details before you start to make it.

6 ERGONOMICS

This is a word you may not have come across before. It is the study of man's performance in any work situation in terms of efficiency and competence. Ergonomists ensure that operations are carried out safely and that tasks are suitable for both man and machine. You have already been involved with ergonomic studies when designing telephones and hairdryers. To be a successful designer you must understand the eventual user. As you know, people come in all shapes and sizes. The study of the measurement of man is known as anthropometrics. This project will introduce you to these two sciences and give you practice in their use.

Controls

There are many different types of controls. Some are operated by the foot, others by the knee or parts of the arm, but most commonly we use our hands. Fingers are used for fine adjustment where little strength is required to operate the control. Finger controls are generally of four different types:

- a smooth continuous adjustment or spinning control
- a switched adjustment where position is not important
- smooth or switched adjustment where some indication of position is helpful but not essential
- switched adjustment where clear indication of position is essential

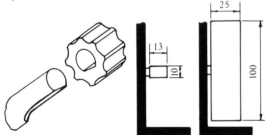

Brief   Design a control knob to meet each of these requirements. The knobs will be mounted on D shaped shafts (see diagram). The maximum and minimum size of the knob is also shown. Then produce orthographic and pictorial views of each knob. Finally make a model of each knob in Placticine or a similar material. Using these models produce a diagram to show the clearance required around each knob to operate it. To do this you will have to design a simple test rig. It is a good idea to produce the chart on squared paper.

Make a sketched study of ten different types of control operated by fingers. Annotate your sketches to highlight the important features.

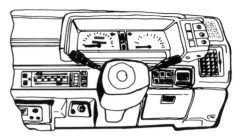

Layout of control panels

The positioning of controls in relation to each other and the operator is important for ease of operation and to avoid error. Panels are designed to follow one or two simple principles:

1   If the operation always follows a fixed sequence the controls and displays should be laid out in that order.

2   If there is not a fixed operating sequence, the controls should be grouped according to their function.

Produce a scale drawing of the layout of a car dashboard. Like the one shown. Analyse the design to see if it follows the above principles. For example, plot the starting sequence or link all the controls relating to one aspect such as maintaining good visibility through the windscreen. (Some controls may be used for a variety of different sequences.)

Now you have carefully examined a dashboard designed by a professional, have a go at designing your own. Firstly list all the controls you will need to include. You may even include functions which you believe will become available in the future. Once you have listed all the controls, cut out paper shapes to represent each one. These shapes can then be used to plan possible designs. Once you have produced your best solution, glue the shapes in position.

Seating

A seat can simply be described as two functional surfaces (see page 31), as shown. Examine a range of chairs, in each case taking the four measurements, w, x, y and z. Classify each chair by its use, for example, office/desk chair, dining chair, armchair. Work out the average measurements for particular types of chairs. With the information you now have produce a pictorial chart which could be used by someone designing seating.

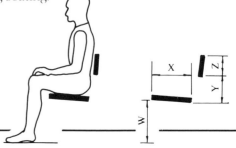

Arrangement of workspace

The efficient layout of workspace can best be examined by producing flow diagrams. Select a working area such as a workshop, storeroom, office or kitchen, then follow this procedure. Produce a scaled plan of the layout. Observe the room in use over a reasonable period of time, recording the number of times journeys are made between particular objects. Record these journeys on your plan as flow lines between the specific objects. The width of the flow line will be determined by the number of journeys recorded. When you have poduced your flow diagram, see if there are ways in which the efficiency of the workspace can be improved.

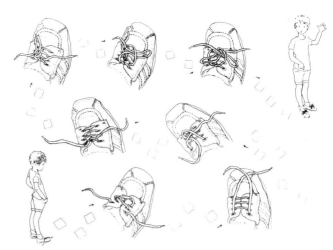

7   A HOME FOR THE 21st CENTURY

What kind of house do you think you will be living in when you are 50? Do you think it will be terraced or semi-detached, made out of brick or concrete, with or without a garage or garden? It will probably be none of these! It seems a long way off, but this is your chance to daydream. Before you start, discuss and exchange ideas with your friends and parents. Ask them what changes they think will take place. It might be a good idea to devise a simple questionnaire. Ask them about the materials from which the house will be made, how it will be heated, what range of rooms will be required, how it will be linked to the outside world, what shape and how large it will be, and so on. When you have all their views, sort out the answers which you think are most likely. Make a ground plan of the dwelling and draw the elevations. Finally, make a model of your design, using the most appropriate materials. You might get some good ideas from science fiction books and films.

8   STORYBOARD

A sequence of pictures is often used to describe how a task or operation is carried out. You might use a storyboard in a case where people do not speak the same language. Another example is the one shown here, a storyboard showing a child how to tie a shoe lace. Produce a storyboard to describe how a particular task is carried out. Choose a practical task such as wiring a plug, changing a hack-saw blade, filling a technical pen, pruning a rose bush, or soldering a circuitboard. If a drawing, such as the shoe, is repeated, remember to use a lightbox. You must tell the story without using words.

9   A NEW PERFUME BOTTLE

You are going to design and model a new perfume bottle and its accompanying graphics and packaging. Start by thinking of a new name. List all the names you know, first of all, and then start adding new ones. Choose the most suitable, perhaps by carrying out some market research. The name will dictate the image and appeal of the final product. When you have a name, you can start a bottle. The bottle design could be done using a computer program. A solids of revolution program would be suitable. Alternatively, it could be designed using sketches and drawings. The final design needs to be made. The body could be turned on a lathe, out of wood or cut from a solid block, and the top could be made from aluminium or brass. Paint the body of the bottle an appropriate colour. A professional designer would make a rubber mould and cast the bottle in an appropriate translucent resin.

When you have finished the bottle and glued on the top, design the pack in which it will be sold. Complete the project by producing all other aspects – the label for the bottle and for the exterior of the pack, colours and style for the lettering etc.

10   DESIGN BRIEF

You now have quite a lot of experience and expertise in graphics. Design and model a graphics unit which would meet your personal requirements. Make detailed working drawings and presentation drawings of the work station. Also, produce a one-sixth scale model of your design, which could be used to demonstrate its features.

INDEX